Already Bad

Volume 1

Episodes 1-5

An original tele/novella
by Michael Frederick

Books by author:

White Shoulders

Places

Ledges

Blue River

The Paper Man

Different

Missouri Madness

Zed

Shy Ann

Drop 50 & Magnify

Summer of '02

Autumn Letters

Stuck

Indie Writer

King of Slugs

Golly Springs

Already Bad/Volume 2

October, 2015/1st printing/2000 copies
Copyright 2015
all rights reserved

Thanks again, Tony, for your art.
Cover Design by Anthony Conrad
Thanks, Paul Coy, for your illustrations.
www.paulcoy.com

Forward:

Tele/novellas are a new way to read an episodic TV series without confusing script directives. It's certainly a different way "to see" fiction - sacrificing narrative for brevity. This format puts my TV and film scripts in the hands of my loyal readers.

I appreciate all feedback on "AB" and welcome your suggestions of actors you would cast to play any of my 5 main characters, a talented American family committed to lowering America's crime rate...one inmate at a time.

Joe Long, the crew's leader, summed up our broken penal system when he addressed the board of directors of the country's largest corporate-owned prison entity: " We consistently sacrifice blood and treasure for wars and invisible fears...while we rot on the inside by neglecting education and rehabilitation."

Pilot Episode:

Joe's Story

I t's night inside the Bingham Correctional Facility, located in rural Kansas 16 miles north of Wichita. It's the state's largest corporate-owned maximum and minimum security correctional facility. Prison inmate JOE LONG is a 55- to 60-year-old, gray-haired, slender Caucasian, who is sitting alone at a picnic table. A yard light shines down on him, illuminating him in his royal blue prison-issue jumpsuit. He smokes an ultra-light American Spirit cigarette while reading from an open file. A guard in the observation tower moves a blinding spotlight around the prison yard and freezes it on Joe, who extends his middle finger in the direction of the tower. Joe has had a tough life, but his life has gained purpose and meaning since being sentenced to Bingham twelve years earlier. It helps that he has had some inside help ever since his best friend from their foster home days in Wichita became a correctional officer at the facility within a year of Joe's incarceration.

Streetwise BOB FULLER—a 55- to 60-year-old, fit African-American—works out alone in the staff fitness room in bare feet, sweatpants, and a tank top while listening to the song "Shame" by Evelyn "Champagne" King. Bob is the senior shift supervisor of the correctional officers at this corporate-owned maximum/minimum security correctional facility. His iPhone vibrates in the pocket of his sweatpants. He turns off the music and we read the text message with him: "Living Legacy tomorrow. Love u, KANSAS." Bob smiles at the message, grabs his towel and shaving kit, and hustles to the shower area.

After showering, Bob is dressed in his correctional officer uniform. Bob quick-shines his black shoes then straightens his hat and tie in mirror. Bob is known by guards and inmates as a no-nonsense guard who can handle any situation. Bob has worked his way up to shift supervisor in this privately owned corporation that owns dozens of correctional facilities across the country.

Shift supervisor Bob walks purposely along the prison hallway recalling why he's here now.

{BOB'S FLASHBACK}:

It's a crisp autumn night in Wichita, Kansas, in 1964. Twelve-year-old BOY JOE wakes up coughing in his twin bed in the small upstairs room he shares with foster brother, Bobby Fuller. The two-story foster home is on fire. Boy Joe checks Bobby's empty bed and rushes out of the room into the smoky hallway. The screaming foster kids and foster parents scrambling to get out of smoke-filled house send an adrenaline rush through all involved.

Outside the burning house, the frantic FOSTER PARENTS count the heads of the shivering FOSTER CHILDREN as fire truck sirens close in. Joe looks around for his best friend but can't see him.

Foster Parent: Joe Long!

Boy Joe: I'm here. Where's Bobby?

Foster Parent: Bobby Fuller! Bobby Fuller?!

Joe looks up to see the light on in the second-floor bathroom window and runs back into the smoke-filled house. BOY BOBBY, twelve, has fallen asleep in his bathwater. Joe hurries to the upstairs bathroom in the smoky house and pounds on the locked bathroom door. Bobby wakes up startled in the cool water and quickly pulls on a pair of pants before opening door. Joe bolts into the bathroom and quickly closes the door behind him, coughing badly. Joe grabs a bath towel and throws it in the tub water, then covers both their heads with dripping wet towel. They put their arms around each other before Joe opens bathroom door and they bolt out of the burning house together.

Boy Joe: Stay with me.

{END OF BOB'S FLASHBACK}

Officer Bob bursts through the door to the prison yard and sees Joe sitting at the same isolated table reading the open file under the light. Bob knows Joe has been waiting for this moment for twelve years as Bob now stands looking down at his best friend. Joe's eyes want good news. This is one of the most important moments of their lives.

Bob: She's on for tomorrow.

Joe looks relieved and points to open file folder he's been reading.

Joe: This would never work without it.

Bob: I know.

The guard in the tower shines the bright spotlight on Bob and holds it there. Bob turns around, drops his pants, and moons the guard in the tower. The light goes away as the two old friends laugh.

Joe: Bobby Ray Fuller, you've been one crazy cat ever since you fell headlong down Mama Annie's basement steps.

The old friends laugh together again.

Bob: Do you think Karen can get that writer?

Joe gets up from table and tosses his cigarette butt in the butt can.

Joe: Brother Bobby, take me home.

Bob unlocks and opens Joe's dark private cell on the minimum-security cell block where all lights are out. After Joe steps into his cell, Bob closes the cell door and turns to leave, but then turns back to Joe to whisper:

Bob: I didn't fall down Mama Annie's steps. You pushed me 'cause I sold your bike for five bucks to Bubba.

Joe: I love you, Bobby.

Bob: I love you, too.

Joe walks over to his desk area with the file folder and turns on the desk light. We see hundreds of file folders and notebooks neatly organized and stacked on the desk and also on shelves above the desk. He looks down at the file in his hand, and we see the title on the cover, Joe's Story, before he files it away with the others. He finds a thin trade-size paperback book by G. K. Fleming titled Indie Writer. He opens the front cover to the author's autographed message: "1/3/2002, Joe, Keep Writing! G. K. Fleming." Joe flips the book over to the back cover where we see a photo of author G. K. Fleming, then a 45- to 50-year old male Caucasian. The author smiles while standing in front of the back end of his mini-motorhome with cynical vehicle lettering that reads "Don't Read My Books" along with his web address www.gkfleming.com.

Joe (to photo): Gary Fleming, you jaded and cynical perfect son-of-a-bitch.

*****

NEXT DAY

On a small-town main street somewhere in northwest Kansas, we see a flyer attached to a makeshift pole sign that's anchored by a truck tire and rim in the middle of the old brick street. A well-maintained 22-foot white Minnie Winnie RV drives up to the sign.

4

The driver looks at the hand-printed flyer: "Indie author G. K. Fleming book signing in library @ 10 A.M. today."

Casually dressed, bearded and bespectacled GARY FLEMING, 55-60, Caucasian author G. K. Fleming—a jaded, dry-humored, self-published author and marketer of twenty-five titles, mostly trade-size paperback novels. Gary frowns at his venue before parking in front of the miniscule library. We see the same cynical vehicle lettering on the back of the RV, "Don't Read My Books / www.gkfleming.com."

*****

Later that afternoon, shade covers Gary's RV, still parked in front of the same small-town library.

Inside the library, only two SENIOR WOMEN attend Gary's book-signing. He sits at the head of a table with three of his titles displayed on the table near his briefcase and laptop. Gary hates the poor showing for his book signing in this dinky town as the seated women haggle over money.

Senior Woman #1: How much for all three?

Gary (fake smile): Twenty-five dollars.

To Gary's chagrin the women discuss splitting the purchase.

Senior Woman #2: We'll take one of each.

Gary: Who do I sign them to?

Senior Woman #1: Flo and Bev.

Gary signs the books fast, hands them to the women, collects his money, and thanks his only customers as they exit the library. The host librarian comes over to Gary, who is not happy with the turnout for his signing. He packs up his things in a hurry to get this experience behind him.

5

Librarian: Sorry about the poor showing. There's a softball tournament …

Gary (cynical): Yeah, yeah. Too bad I'm not selling pizza or beer. Oh, that reminds me. You mentioned I'd get a free meal at the café …

*****

Later, seated at a window table in the café, Gary has eaten and writes in longhand with a pencil on an elevated black-leather writing folder supplied with typing paper. An open road atlas is on the table.

Gary (voice over writing): *Lousy signing today in a small Kansas town by the Colorado border. Sold three books to a couple of spinsters. I'm off to Burlington, Colorado, to settle an old debt. Looking forward to my annual Country Acres fundraiser and book signing in Garden City, where I do better every year. No more signings in libraries. I'm too old for this crap.*

*****

Meanwhile, in Garden City, Kansas, an older model station wagon pulls into the parking lot of Country Acres, a modern senior-living facility. The station wagon parks purposely quite a distance from the front entrance. There's a bunch of camera equipment on the bed of the old car. KANSAS (former name KAREN LONG) is a 30-year-old Caucasian recovering drug addict who has been sober for twelve years. Faded floral tattoos cover both arms. Kansas is attractive and smart, a struggling waitress/documentary filmmaker who has raised her baby brother alone these last twelve years. She straightens her short hair in the mirror then flips down the visor to reveal a highlighted three-by-five card with neat lettering: "There's plenty of money in the universe." She closes her eyes and repeats:

Kansas: There's plenty of money in the universe.

6

Kansas has always lived like a "Bargain Betty," shopping at thrift stores for her and her brother's clothes. Outside her car she quickly puts on a long-sleeve blouse to hide her tattoos. She gets her camera equipment and shoulder bags holding the tools of her trade from the back of the wagon and carries it all toward the front entrance of the nicest retirement home in town.

*****

Meanwhile, Gary's moving RV passes the Colorado state line.

*****

Soon, Gary carries a duffel bag that holds the tools of his trade as he walks along a downtown Burlington sidewalk and enters a small independently owned bookstore. Gary finds and removes from a bookshelf four different titles by G. K. Fleming and walks to the counter peeling off the price stickers. The BOOKSTORE OWNER is a man in his 70s whom Gary has never met, yet he reminds Gary of every deadbeat bookstore owner that delayed or withheld payment from him. Gary continues peeling off price stickers at the counter.

Bookstore Owner: Find what you were looking for?

Gary: I sure did.

The bookstore owner watches Gary remove the price stickers and put the four books inside his bag.

Bookstore Owner: I need to scan those.

Gary: You never paid me for these books. Bye, asshole.

Gary exits the store with his books in his bag. Half a block down, Gary sees a beauty shop owner reading in her salon.

{SERIES OF SHOTS}:

7

Gary removes four books from his bag and shows them to the beauty shop owner

Soon, Gary signs all four books for $15.00 cash and thanks her.

Gary feels pretty good now as he walks with a purpose along the sidewalk.

{END SERIES OF SHOTS}

*****

At the open doorway to a resident's private room marked "Mary Hope," Kansas, carrying her camera equipment and laptop case, is ushered into the room by JANE MORGAN. Jane is the middle-aged daughter of MARY HOPE, the 80-something-year-old matriarch and sole owner of Garden City Motors. Mary is seated in one of two chairs in front of the window wearing a dress suit and a sweet smile.

Jane: Mom, this is Kansas, the young lady who will interview us for our Living Legacy DVD.

Kansas: Hi, Mary. After I check the lighting and set up my camera, I'll be asking you and Jane a few questions about your lives. It'll be fun.

As Kansas sets up her camera for interview:

Jane: It's uncanny how my husband, John, and I were just talking about doing something like this with Mom when you called.

Kansas: So your husband won't be here?

Jane: He's behind on his sales quota this month and has to stay at the dealership. He wants you to feel free to go down there to interview him if you want.

Kansas nods while setting up a shot behind her digital camera on a tripod.

Jane: Kansas, don't you have a brother?

Kansas: Kenny! He graduates tomorrow.

Jane: That's wonderful! Does he have plans for college?

Kansas: He's not sure what he wants to do. Right now he's into advertising.

The wind picks up outside Mary's window.

*****

Curbside, outside a Garden City fast-food chicken restaurant, totally disguised in a yellow chicken costume is KENNY LONG, 18, younger brother of Kansas. Kenny flaps his wings in the wind to attract passing motorists from the sidewalk.

*****

Meanwhile, Gary is seated and writing with a pencil at a front patio table of a Burlington, Colorado, coffeehouse. He has covered his cup of coffee with a napkin to keep it warm. His laptop is open on the table, and the black bag is slung over an empty chair. The tools of his trade are out of the bag: a Total Pillow cushions his lower back, an empty eyeglasses case elevates his writing folder, and a pocket dictionary and open atlas are on the table. As Gary writes, the pencil end breaks off and he adroitly blunts the pencil end under the tabletop. He opens the folder and gets a new pencil from the compartment. He takes a wincing sip of cold coffee and looks across the street at a retail marijuana dispensary with a line of customers waiting to get in. Gary goes back to writing.

Gary (voice over writing): *I've lost my interest in fiction because my life has stopped being interesting to me. After thirty*

9

*years of this, I know I could retire near my dad in the desert and
live frugally with my dull habits. Yet I would know I had failed to
become a writer/in, a published author whose work is in demand.
I've spent my energy filling pages with words I alone could string
together but nobody wanted. As I approach sixty, I promise myself
here and now that I will live my life as a writer/in.*

Gary stops writing and looks across the street at the crowded
dispensary. He scoffs at the line and continues writing.

*****

Back in Mary Hope's private room in Garden City's Country Acres,
Kansas is behind the camera interviewing the Garden City Motors
women seated together holding hands in front of Mary's window.

　　Kansas: Mary, tell Jane one of your favorite memories of her
while growing up.

　　Mary Hope: So many holidays were such fun …

Behind Mary through the camera lens Kansas can see the wind has
picked up considerably as:

*****

Kenny, in his chicken suit, tries to fly in a strong wind gust as:

*****

Gary's table is cleared. Across the street we see Gary waiting in
line to buy pot legally. He wears sunglasses with his bag slung over
his shoulder as:

*****

Kansas interviews the women with the camera on. Kansas stands
behind her camera.

Kansas: Mary, you had a son named Jerry who passed away eight years ago. Tell us about Jerry.

Mother and daughter eye each other warily then burst into laughter.

Kansas: What's so funny?

Mary: Jerry was a good son. He worked hard.

Jane: And he played even harder.

The women laugh and nod in agreement as Kansas seems happy too.

Mary: No, but Jerry did make the dealership what it is today.

Kansas: Who manages Garden City Motors now that Jerry's gone?

Jane: My husband, John Morgan, has been the general manager since Jerry died.

Kansas: Mary, share with us a fond memory of Jerry.

*****

Gary exits the marijuana retail store wearing sunglasses as Christopher Cross sings "Sailing," a song in Gary's CD collection that plays through:

{SERIES OF SHOTS}:

Gary walks briskly to his RV, gets behind the wheel, and drives away.

Gary, with a toothpick in his mouth, drives to I-70 eastbound and smiles at the bag beside him.

Gary's RV passes the Kansas state line marker. The wind increases markedly.

11

Kenny, in his chicken costume, is blown down by strong winds.

Gary pulls off the Interstate into a parking area because of the strong winds and poor visibility.

A bit later, we see Kenny's sweaty face as he eats his lunch in the break room.

{END SERIES OF SHOTS}

*****

Gary is parked at a rural Kansas parking area as the song winds down and stops. The wind is down, and so is Gary's back door step. The main back door is open and the screen door behind the main door is latched shut. Inside the RV is the sound of an overhead bathroom fan scraping on a screen until Gary, in boxers and a t-shirt, inserts a toothpick near the turn crank for smooth running. He tests his recent purchase with a pipe and exhales into the fan. We see that the shower stall holds several cases of his inventory of books. Panning into the living space of the RV, we see more cases of books stacked in various places. Gary opens the overhead storage area, and we see a row of small-town phone books. He locates the Garden City phone book and places it on the bed over the cab. He picks up his cell phone and dons a headset while standing in the aisle. Opening the phone book, we see extensive notations next to the listing. Gary picks up a handheld magnifier and dials the first phone number.

Gary (on phone to voicemail): Mrs. Frank! This is G. K. Fleming, the indie writer. Once again I'm calling to remind you of my fifteenth annual fundraiser at Country Acres this Saturday at two. Five dollars of every book sold goes right to the retirement home. Hope to see you again with friends!

Gary makes a quick notation and dials the next number, making an effort to sound positive.

12

Gary: Mrs. Franklin! This is author G. K. Fleming!

*****

Kenny gets off work and walks home in jeans and a t-shirt. He's tired.

*****

Mary and Jane watch and enjoy their finished interview for Living Legacy on Kansas's laptop screen.

*****

Gary's RV is parked alone in the same spot. Gary naps on the couch with his feet elevated for circulation. We see his recent pages on the writing folder on the table and hear Gary's words he's written.

Gary (voice over): *I'm jaded from calling my own readers in Garden City. I'm tired and must change. I just can't write another book and sell it myself. Change is coming.*

*****

Kansas leaves Mary's room carrying her equipment. She stops and goes back to Mary's room as if she forgot something but stops short of Mary's open door and overhears their conversation:

Jane (off screen): That poor girl, Kansas, and her brother. To live in a small town after your father did what he did.

Mary (o. s.): Yes, what a terrible thing to go through.

Kansas heads for the front entrance of Country Acres and discreetly removes Gary's posted flyer before exiting the building with it and her equipment.

13

Soon, Kansas sits behind the wheel of her old station wagon in the Country Acres parking lot and stares down at the flyer flattened against the steering wheel. We see a picture of G. K. Fleming on the flyer announcing the upcoming fundraiser. She reaches for and pulls down the visor to display the same three-by-five card. She closes her eyes:

Kansas: There's plenty of money in the universe.

*****

Kenny walks across the parking lot of the Garden City Motel/Café, his home for the last twelve years. He unlocks and enters the motel room where he and his sister Kansas live. Their room has two queen-size beds, a fridge, and a microwave; it looks like a small studio apartment. He quickly dons his kelly-green cap and graduation gown to see how he looks in the mirror before showering.

Showered and dressed in jeans and a t-shirt, lean Kenny walks to an isolated parking area behind the motel and uses his key to open the door of a 1964 sixteen-foot Shasta travel trailer. Inside the trailer, Kenny opens a window above the bed and gets a pot pipe and stash from his hiding place. He lights the pipe, inhales, holds it in, and exhales smoke out the window before lying back on the bed.

{KENNY'S FLASHBACK}:

It's 2007 inside a prison viewing area. BOY KENNY is ten and Kansas is twenty-two. They stand behind one-way glass about to enter the visiting area to see Joe for the first time since he killed their mother four years earlier. Now they see Joe take a seat behind the glassed-in visiting area in the next room. Joe can't see them. Correctional officer Bob enters the room in his uniform and kneels down to little Kenny with Kansas standing beside her brother.

Bob: Kenny, you don't have to see your dad now. Would you rather wait here for Karen-

Kansas: Kansas. My name is Kansas.

Bob: Whatever.

Kansas (to Kenny): He's right, Kenny. You don't have to see him now. I'll tell you everything he says. I promise. Okay?

Boy Kenny nods yes and watches his sister exit the room with Bob. Kenny watches them through the one-way glass.

Bob helps Kansas with her chair as she sits facing her stepdad with glass between them. Joe puts his palm on glass but Kansas defiantly does not return the gesture. Contrite Joe puts his hand down.

Joe: Hey, Karen.

Kansas: My name is Kansas.

They sit in awkward silence until Kansas cuts to chase:

Kansas: I know why you did it. She told you the truth about Kenny. You got in a fight. She died.

Joe is contrite.

Kansas: Why didn't you just leave?

Joe is sorry he didn't leave and says nothing.

Kansas: Kenny is not to know why you did it or any of the details. I told him you'll tell him yourself after he graduates from high school.

Joe agrees with a contrite nod.

Kansas: It might mess him up more than it already has.

Another nod from contrite Joe, then:

15

Joe: Is he here?

Kansas: He doesn't want to see you now.

Joe: How's he holding up?

Kansas: About as well as any boy whose mother was killed by his father.

Joe: Why don't you move out of that town?

Kansas: Where would we go? I've got a good job at the Garden City Motel/Cafe. We live there. I wait tables and clean rooms. I like it there.

She sees that Joe is sorry and genuinely concerned about them.

Kansas: Look, Joe…we're fine. People are good to us there.

Joe: So you came back from L. A. when you heard?

Kansas: I was two months into rehab and I had to finish another month there to get out. It was the longest month of my life. They put Kenny in a county foster home until I got custody in six weeks. That job saved us. Kenny has helped me stay sober all this time.

Understanding nod from Joe.

Kansas: Why did you plea-bargain for twenty years without parole instead of a trial by jury?

Joe: A trial would've been tough on Kenny and wouldn't bring his mother back. (beat) Why'd you come here?

Kansas: To ask you not to write Kenny or me any more letters until we want to write you.

Joe gives her an understanding nod. Kansas feels compassion for Joe.

16

Kansas: Maybe we can visit at Christmas. Or your birthday. Or at least I can. I can't speak for Kenny. (changes subject) I sold Mom's house. We never lived in it after uh…

Joe: How much did you get for it?

Kansas: Twenty thousand.

Joe: That's pretty good for that cracker box.

Kansas: It's in a savings account for Kenny. I told him I'd give it all to him after he graduates.

Behind one-way glass Kenny watches his sister and dad.

{END OF KENNY'S FLASHBACK}

Kenny gets up from the bed in the Shasta trailer and finds an old newspaper article from 2001 with a picture of Joe being awarded a plaque from Jerry Hope with headline: Garden City Motors Employee of the Year.

*****

Kansas, still parked in the Country Acres lot, hesitates before sending Gary an email message from his web page that we don't see. She flips down her visor to read her mantra:

Kansas: There's plenty of money …

Kansas takes a deep breath and sends the message.

*****

That night, Joe sits on his bed holding a letter from Kenny that he's read several times. We see Kenny's high school graduation announcement card standing on Joe's cluttered writing table. Once again he reads the letter.

17

Kenny (voice over): *I know you can't come to my graduation.
I'm not sure I'd want you to. The card proves I graduated. Kansas
has been planning for me to visit you soon after I graduate. We're
supposed to do the last scene for Joe's Story. I'm not looking
forward to that. Kansas says it will be a healing thing for both of
us. See you soon, Kenny.*

Joe lies back on his bed with the letter on his chest thinking back to
that day and night he lost it.

{JOE'S FLASHBACK}:

In 2003, Joe, 45, wears a service manager's uniform and stands with
a clipboard at the service bay entrance to Garden City Motors. A
brand new 2003 car pulls up to Joe, driven by Joe's boss, JERRY
HOPE, a 45- to 50-year-old flashy dresser. Jerry leaves the door
open to the idling car while walking away from Joe. Joe hates Jerry
because Joe's wife and Jerry had once been lovers. Joe knows that
Jerry is Karen's biological father, but Jerry never claimed Karen as
his daughter. It's a small town.

Jerry: Joe, have my car detailed and ready in an hour! Okay,
buddy?

Joe (mutters to clipboard): Just for you, boss man.

Joe gets into Jerry's idling car and closes the door. Right away Joe
smells his wife's perfume. He sees ashtray crammed with lipstick-
stained Marlboro Lights—his wife's brand. Angry, Joe opens the
console and finds the CD cover to Don Henley's Actual Miles with
the CD cover depicting Henley as slick car salesman. Joe is angry.

*****

That night, we see a small, single-story Garden City home in a
lower-middle-class neighborhood. The lights are on in the front
window. Joe in casual clothes sits in his recliner with a mixed drink
and a cigarette. He's stewing over what he found in Jerry's car

earlier. In the kitchen, BONNIE LONG, a 35- to 40-year-old attractive party gal and Joe's wife of seven years, stands at the kitchen counter making a mixed drink while her lipstick-stained Marlboro Light burns in an ashtray on the counter next to her. Joe gets out of his recliner and staggers to the stack of CDs; he can't find the CD he's looking for.

Joe (calls to kitchen): Bonnie, where's the Don Henley CD?

Bonnie: Isn't it there with the others? Unless Karen took it to California!

Joe: She wouldn't just take it!

Bonnie: My alcoholic, pill-popping daughter? That's my guess!

Joe's jaw is clenched in anger.

{END OF JOE'S FLASHBACK}

Joe's lies down on his bed in his private cell.

*****

That night, Gary's RV is dark inside and still parked at the same rural Kansas parking area. Gary wakes up from a nap on his couch; he turns on the light, dons his glasses and opens his laptop on the table. He checks the time on his cell phone and gets handful of mixed nuts from fridge before he sees on the laptop screen that he has a message from "livinglegacybyks". He opens the message and reads it with increasing interest.

*****

Kenny sits at a table with his sister having a late supper in the café where Kansas works as a waitress. Kansas is working and wearing her uniform. Kenny's not hungry. He's dreading the upcoming last scene with Joe in his sister's documentary.

19

Kansas: Tomorrow's the big day. Are you excited?

Kenny nods while picking at his plate with his fork.

Kenny: Excited about graduating ... but not about what comes after that.

Kansas: You know I have to shoot that last scene.

Kenny: I know! For the millionth time!

Kansas: That's the plan. The plan you've known about for how long now? You haven't told anybody, have you?

Kenny: Why would I? You've been telling me for how long? That I only get Mom's money from the house if I graduate and after I ask Dad on camera why he killed Mom!

Karen: You're anxious about it.

Kenny: Duh! Hell yeah, I'm anxious! I don't want to relive that!

He gets an understanding nod from his big sister.

Kenny: This isn't some character in a play. It's real and it's a hard thing to think about for twelve years.

Kansas understands and puts her hand on her brother's hand.

Kansas: I know. And I also know that doing this will free you.

Kenny: More like the twenty grand will free me.

Kansas laughs a bit then plays big sister, discreetly.

Kansas: When you get your money you are not running off to California like I did just to get high.

Kenny: I won't have to. Colorado's legal.

Kansas: Twenty-one, buster.

Kenny: Three years isn't that long.

Kansas gets up and buses the table.

Kenny: You closing tonight?

Kansas: Yeah, and I told Jean I'm out of here at nine. You staying in tonight?

Kenny: Yeah. I might go for a walk later. It helps me sleep.

Kansas: I know, sweetie.

She kisses Kenny on the forehead and carries the dishes to the kitchen.

*****

A light is on behind the closed curtain of the bed over the cab of the RV, which is still parked at the same rural rest area. Gary, in boxers and a t-shirt, writes up a storm.

Gary (voice over writing): *In Burlington I tried to write more lies in my next novel. Nothing. Then I bought a little Blue Nugget and changed my thought patterns. Traveller is parked at this lonely Kansas rest area. Good weed. It makes me want to be around people. Got an email from this woman named Kansas who makes documentaries. She invited me to her brother's high school graduation tomorrow. She says if I show, she'll film my signing at Country Acres for free and guarantees my best signing ever. I know I can't keep doing these small-town gigs and ever expect to be a writer/in—a real writer who doesn't have to peddle my own books. I have a thousand books with me, and if she's right ... I'm in.*

*****

21

Kenny stands on the sidewalk. The lights are on in the front room of the house that used to be his mother's.

Kenny (voice over): I know the past doesn't run me now. I graduate tomorrow. Then I go see Joe. I know Kansas has been making her documentary to pay me the money she had to spend to support me. I have to do this thing with Joe. I owe that much to her.

Kenny walks away.

*****

NEXT DAY

The high school auditorium is full for graduation. At the foot of the stage Kansas has her camera on Kenny in his cap and gown as he approaches the principal to receive his diploma.

Announcer: Kenny Long!

The audience applauds for Kenny. Gary applauds as he watches Kansas film her brother until he is off the stage where she tearfully embraces him.

*****

Outside the school's front entrance, Gary stands on the sidewalk facing the exiting, happy graduates. Kansas and Kenny carry the camera equipment outside. Kansas sees Gary before Gary sees her, and she ducks out of Gary's view, pulling Kenny with her. She's excited.

Kansas: He's here! I can't believe ... No, I do believe. There is abundance in the universe!

Kenny: You're nuts.

Kansas: Kenny, that's the same author who Joe wants to run our film crew.

Kenny: Really?

Kansas: Just meet him and split.

They approach Gary.

Kansas: Mr. Fleming?

Gary: You must be Kansas. Please call me Gary. Congratulations, Kenny.

After shaking hands, Kenny excuses himself to meet friends. Kenny tries to hand Kansas her the tripod and the laptop in the shoulder-strapped carrying case but Gary intercepts him.

Gary: I got it. I'm parked at the café.

Kansas: Me, too. I waitress there.

They start walking.

Gary: Country Acres reserved a room for me there Friday night.

Kansas: I know. I took the reservation.

Gary: Really?

Kansas: I work the desk now and then. My brother and I have lived in the motel for twelve years.

Gary: Really? How did that happen?

Kansas: That's all in my documentary, Joe's Story. I'd so love for you to see my documentary, Mr. Fleming ... I mean, Gary.

Gary: I must admit your email got my attention.

Kansas: I was thinking how I could tell you this if you came or if I talked to you at Country Acres. It must be easy for you to sum up a story. I'll cut to the chase. Our mother was killed twelve years ago by Kenny's dad, who is my stepdad. It's confusing, I know.

Gary (stops walking): That's awful! Why did he do it?

Kansas: That's what the last scene in Joe's Story is about. I'm going to film Kenny with Joe in Bingham Prison. Joe's going to tell Kenny why he killed his mother.

Gary: Now that's big drama.

They continue walking.

Kansas: I've been working on it for six years. It's mostly about Kenny's life, how he's refused to play the victim for his parents' mistakes.

Gary: So this guy, Joe …

Kansas: Joe Long.

Gary: Do you know why Joe killed your mother?

Kansas: Yes.

Gary: May I ask why?

Kansas: Because she was screwing Joe's boss, the same man who was my biological father and, for that matter, Kenny's. I believe she was drunk that night with Joe, and she told him that Jerry Hope was Kenny's father. My mom got pregnant with me long before she met Joe. I was about ten when my mom married Joe. Joe adopted me after Kenny was born.

Gary: Kansas Long?

Kansas: It was Karen Long. I changed my name to Kansas.

24

Gary: Were you and Kenny at home when it happened?

Kansas: I was in L. A. in rehab. Kenny was at home.

They near the Garden City Café/Motel parking lot where Traveller, Gary's RV is parked.

Gary: So where did Joe work?

Kansas stops walking and looks in the direction of Garden City Motors, a large car dealership located across the street from the café/motel where she has worked and lived for twelve years. Gary and Kansas stand on the sidewalk while looking at the dealership across the street.

Kansas: Joe was the service manager at Garden City Motors. Jerry Hope was the owner and general manager.

Gary: Was?

Kansas: Jerry died of a heart attack a few years after my mom died.

Gary: So Jerry and your mom were longtime sex buddies?

Kansas: Right.

Gary: Who owns Garden City Motors now?

Kansas: Mary Hope, Jerry's mother. She's one of your loyal readers.

Gary: I recognize the name. Did Jerry know he was your and Kenny's biological father?

Kansas: My mother told him. Jerry gave her money all the time. He bought her a house and gave her trade-ins every year free and clear. She never worked. Jerry supported her until she married Joe.

Gary: But your mom kept seeing Jerry.

Kansas: Yeah. Many times she told me that Kenny was Jerry's kid. I left when Kenny was four. I got tired of living around her lies.

Gary: So Joe lost it when she told him.

Kansas: I'd bet on it.

They walk toward Gary's parked RV.

Later, inside the RV, Gary and Kansas sit across the table from each other watching Joe's Story on her laptop. Upon seeing the interview with Mary Hope and her daughter, Jane, Gary motions for Kansas to pause her documentary.

Gary: This is the interview Joe had you do?

Kansas: Right.

Gary gets up and paces slowly back and forth in Traveller.

Gary: I have to meet this Joe Long. You say he's been interviewing inmates for twelve years. How does he get access to do all this in prison?

Kansas: He told me he started talking to inmates to get out of his head. Within a few months he solved two cold cases involving missing persons. The families were so grateful to finally have closure they visited Joe in prison to personally thank him. Warden Ted loves Joe.

Gary: That's amazing. So you got out of rehab and never got any help from Jerry Hope?

Kansas: He died a few years after I got back. The past is dead.

Gary: But Garden City Motors isn't.

Kansas: That's what Joe says. Garden City Motors will buy the documentary to keep their good public image.

Gary: And Jerry Hope is finally made culpable for his part in this tragedy. It's beautiful.

Gary opens the curtains and we can see the dealership across the street. Gary sits on the couch while Kansas packs up her laptop.

Gary: Kansas, why do you want me to buy your documentary?

Kansas: Two reasons: I sold my mom's house for twenty thousand and promised Kenny the money when he graduates as long as he does the final scene in my documentary.

Gary: You spent the money.

She nods yes.

Gary: What's the other reason?

Kansas: Joe wants you to manage our film crew.

Gary is shocked by this as Kansas has an incoming call on her cell phone.

Gary: Like a director?

Positive nod from Kansas, then she answers her cell phone.

Kansas (into phone): I'll be right there. (To Gary) I have to go. We go see Joe tomorrow to shoot the last scene. It's a three-hour drive to Bingham. You want to go with us?

Gary: I'm in.

Kansas: Great. You're welcome to join us in the cafe for a free buffet …to celebrate Kenny's graduation.

Gary: Thanks. I am a little hungry.

Gary watches Kansas leave with her equipment and walk to her room. Gary goes into his bathroom and inserts a toothpick into the overhead fan crank before turning on the fan and getting his pipe and stash from the bathroom cabinet.

Gary exits the RV wearing sunglasses after getting stoned. He locks the back door and pauses to look across the street at the dealership that could bring the new life he's looking for.

*****

Kenny and Kansas are in casual clothes sitting at a booth in the café dining area. Kansas eats but Kenny isn't hungry because he's anxious about his upcoming scene with Joe.

Kansas: No pressure … but you and Joe have to be good or Gary won't buy.

Kenny: Yeah … no pressure …right. I've decided to give you half the money from Mom's house.

Kansas is shocked by her brother's words.

Kenny: So you can give up waitressing and we can do these stories with Joe like he wants. You can get a better car, a second camera. You always say you need two cameras.

Kansas: If Gary buys …

Kansas sees Gary wearing sunglasses with a plate of food; she waves him over. Gary sits beside Kansas.

Kenny: I hear you're going with us tomorrow.

Gary: Wouldn't miss it.

As Gary eats, Kenny spots some friends and leaves the table to join them.

Kenny: See you, Gary.

Gary waves goodbye and stays seated next to Kansas.

Kansas: So you'll ride with us?

Gary: I'll see if I can park Traveller at Country Acres.

Kansas: You can park in back of the motel by my trailer as long as you want. I'll tell the manager. Nobody will bother you back there.

Gary: Thank you.

Kansas: You call your RV Traveller?

Gary: I named it after Robert E. Lee's horse. I wanted to give my only home and transportation a reliable name.

Kansas: My car, it's a real junker. I park it in back with Shasta, my travel trailer, so customers don't think we're a dive motel.

Gary: It can't be that bad.

*****

After Gary parks Traveller by Shasta and the old station wagon, he walks over to Kansas who is leaning against her car.

Gary: Why don't we take Traveller?

Kansas agrees, laughing.

*****

That night in Traveller, Gary reads on the sofa with his legs elevated and his feet against the wall. He smells something familiar. Gary gets up and peers from behind the closed curtain at a candle flickering behind the open window of Shasta. He smiles and goes back to reading.

*****

NEXT DAY

We see Traveller rolling on a Kansas highway. Gary drives while
Kenny lies on the couch listening to music with earbuds inserted.
Kansas sits at the table editing on her laptop.

*****

Joe nervously smokes a cigarette alone by the prison yard fence.
He's looking beyond the fence at his worst moments of temporary
insanity that sent him here for twenty years.

{JOE'S FLASHBACK}:

It's 2003, the same night Joe asked Bonnie about the missing Don
Henley CD. Joe and Bonnie have been drinking and arguing in the
front room. Joe sits in his recliner and Bonnie is on the sofa.

Bonnie: Before we got married I told you Jerry Hope is Karen's
biological father! You keep throwing that in my face! How do you
think I got all those expensive clothes in my closet? You can't
handle the fact that Jerry bought this house and gives me a new car
trade-in every year without paying a dime!

Joe (angry hushed tone): Keep your voice down!

Bonnie gets up and goes into the kitchen to make another drink. Joe
gets up, staggers to a closed bedroom door, opens it, and sees Boy
Kenny, 6, sleeping in bed. Joe closes the door quietly and goes into
the kitchen where Bonnie is drinking. Her lipstick-stained
Marlboro Light is burning in the ashtray next to her.

Bonnie (spiteful laugh): You really think I'd have any of my
nice things on your salary? And do you really believe you'd have
that job that I asked Jerry to give you?

This is hurtful, stunning news to Joe.

30

Bonnie: Service manager? You couldn't get a good job like that on your own.

Joe sees her lipstick-stained cigarette butts in the ashtray and angrily grabs her upper arm. He pins her to the counter and confronts her about her affair with Jerry Hope.

Joe: I found your Don Henley CD in Jerry's car! Along with your cigarette butts! I could smell your perfume! It reeked so bad I almost puked!

Bonnie (yanking her arm free): Keep your hands off me!

Joe grabs Bonnie and pins her against the fridge.

Joe (in her face): Yes, I knew you and Jerry were sex buddies and that Karen was his kid. You promised me it was over!

Bonnie knees Joe in the groin. Joe falls to the kitchen floor writhing in agony. Bonnie stands over Joe and delivers a shocker:

Bonnie (yelling): You're not half the man he is! And in more ways than one! You don't even see that Kenny looks more like Jerry than Karen does?

Joe incredulously looks up at Bonnie from the kitchen floor in a drunken stupor.

Bonnie: Yeah, that's right.

Joe (stunned whisper): Kenny ... is Jerry's kid?

Bonnie: Even Karen knows it! You don't have a clue, Joe Long!

Temporary insanity takes over. Joe tackles Bonnie to the floor, mounts her, and starts covering her mouth as if to shut her up. Bonnie has a massive coronary and dies instantly with her eyes open. He tries to revive her with mouth-to-mouth in vain. Joe struggles to the sink where he soaks his head in cold water to sober up. He dials 911.

Joe (on the kitchen phone): Send an ambulance to 211 Howard Street.

Joe passes out on the kitchen floor beside Bonnie's dead body.

{END OF JOE'S FLASHBACK}

Joe is smoking a cigarette by the prison yard fence. He walks the fence line.

Joe (voice over): *That's all I can tell him. And that I deserved twenty years for causing her death. In here I've found something special that can keep my kids in my life while I'm doing my time. I'm thankful for that. And what's this "Kansas" baloney? Her name's Karen to me. But she was right: I should've just left ... like Karen did.*

*****

Gary is behind the wheel of moving Traveller as Kansas and Kenny sit at the table going over the upcoming scene with Joe. Gary is listening to his Chris Rhea CD with the volume low so he can eavesdrop on them.

Kansas (directing Kenny): You have to ask Joe why he killed Mom.

Kenny nods yes.

Gary (turning off music): Hey, Kenny!

Kenny gets up and leans in to the front cab area.

Gary: Would you please get me a cold Zevia and three aspirin in the bathroom cabinet?

32

Kenny: Sure.

When Gary sees in the rearview mirror that Kenny is in the bathroom, Gary snaps his fingers to get Kansas to come up to him. She does.

Gary (eyes in rearview mirror): You have got to be sure Joe mentions Jerry Hope's name or this won't sell. I won't even think of buying your story unless the unpunished-but-dead Jerry Hope is made at least partly responsible for your mother's death and Joe's incarceration. You understand?

Kansas gives Gary a thumbs up as Kenny arrives with three aspirin and an opened can of soda. Gary swallows the aspirin with the soda.

Kenny: I could use some aspirin.

Gary: Help yourself.

In the closed bathroom when Kenny gets the aspirin for himself from the cabinet, he finds Gary's pipe and stash he bought in Colorado.

*****

Meanwhile, the Bingham inmates return to their cells on Joe's cell block. Uniformed, unarmed correctional officer Bob walks over to Joe's cell. Bob is a shift supervisor of guards.

Bob: You ready for your interview with Kenny?

Joe: I think so. Bobby, I've been interviewing the worst of the worst here for twelve years. This is the first one that scares me.

Bob: We'll all be watching.

Joe: I couldn't do this without you.

33

Bob: I know.

They both laugh. As Bob walks away:

Joe: Bobby?

Bob turns back to his best friend and moves closer to listen.

Joe: There's something in my private locker I want you to get.

*****

Meanwhile, Kansas and Kenny sit across from Gary; they're having breakfast in a truck stop café. Kenny still doesn't have an appetite and gets up from the table as if to use the restroom.

Gary (eating): You think he's ready to do this?

Kansas (eating): I hope so.

Gary: I'm a bit anxious, myself. I've been writing fiction for forty years…but this is real stuff here.

Kansas: Gary, do you believe in the law of attraction?

Gary: As in you get what you reflect?

Kansas: Sort of. It's a universal law that says if you have a problem, you give your attention to the solution to the problem.

Gary nods in agreement while chewing.

Kansas: I believe you are the solution to my problem.

Gary: I'm the solution? I think your brother and Joe are the solution.

Kansas: Could I get sued for making this documentary?

Gary: Not if it's true … and not if you don't own it. (leans closer) I think you want to get that son-of-a-bitch, Jerry Hope, for his part in this. And, of course, you want twenty grand to cover Kenny. (leans back) And here I am, sitting across from my universal law of attraction. (leans forward again) I'll get the money you need, and a little more for me, and I'll save Garden City Motors a hell of a lot more than they'll pay me to make sure their former service manager's story is never seen.

Kansas: How much do you think you can get?

Gary: I'm not sure I'll even buy your documentary, Kansas. It all depends on this last scene. (pushing his plate away) Or you try to get the money to produce and market the DVD yourself. Until then, you watch all those new cars driving off the lot across the street year after year while you're busting your ass waiting tables and living in a motel room with your brother.

Gary's haughty smile irritates Kansas as he picks up the tab, checks it, leaves a tip, and looks around the room for Kenny.

Kansas: Would you consider marketing the DVD yourself?

Gary (negative nod): Too much work for a man my age.

*****

A bit later, outside the truck stop café, standing in front of Traveller, Kansas and Gary look for Kenny.

Gary: Maybe he's still in the restroom.

They hear laughter coming from the back of Traveller. They walk back to see Kenny stoned, wearing shades, and leaning against Traveller's back ladder.

Kansas: What were you laughing at?

Kenny (points to vehicle lettering): It's the last irony and brilliant (laughs) It's the perfect cynical statement for apathy. I get it.

Kenny applauds Gary while laughing.

Kansas: Gary, would you excuse us for a minute?

Big sister waits until Gary gets behind the wheel to scold her baby brother.

Kansas (in Kenny's face): You promised not to bring any weed!

Kenny: I didn't! I took a pinch of his stash in the bathroom.

Kansas (angry whisper): That's stealing! And from a man who could get us out of poverty. And this scene ... the one we've been planning for eight years? You want to play it stoned? Or maybe a big laugh would be good when Joe spills his guts to you on camera? I've been supporting you for twelve years and you are not going to blow this opportunity we have.

Kenny (contritely confessing): I've been dreading this day most of my life. And now it's here. I didn't want to feel afraid like I was when it first happened.

Kansas gives Kenny some money from her jeans pocket.

Kansas: Go buy some eye drops and gum. Give me your weed.

Kenny gives her a roach from his back pocket that she grinds on the pavement with her shoe.

Kenny (walking away): What a waste of good weed.

Kansas walks over to Gary's open window.

Gary: Is he okay?

Kansas: Yeah. He's just freaked out about the scene with Joe.
He's fine.

*****

In Bingham's massive dining room, Joe sits at a table alone with a
headache and no appetite. WARDEN TED, a 60- to 65-year-old
conservative type with a dry sense of humor and not much of a
mean streak, sits down across from Joe with his cup of coffee.
Warden Ted is a believer in Joe's work and knows this is his big
day with his son. And it doesn't hurt that Joe Long is advancing the
warden's career in positive ways.

Joe: Hey, Warden Ted.

Warden Ted: You got everything you need?

Joe: Yeah, thanks.

Warden Ted: Joe, I got a call from one of our wardens in
Nebraska who wants to come down here and consult with you about
your Living Legacy for our inmates. I told her -

Joe: Her? It's a women's penitentiary? (smiles) I'm in!

Warden: I told her I'd check with you first.

Joe: Sounds good to me. You know where to find me.

Warden Ted (gets up to leave): Good luck today with Kenny.

Joe: Thank you, sir.

*****

Traveller rolls down the highway with Gary behind the wheel while
Kenny lies on the couch with one earbud inserted listening to music.
Gary grabs his cell phone and talks into it as if he's a tour guide,
loud and friendly:

37

Gary: Approaching Bingham Correctional Facility, a maximum and minimum security prison, home of the second largest maximum security prison in The Sunflower State! We'll be stopping to tour the prison in about nine minutes! I suggest you keep your seat belts fastened and avoid hitchhikers!

Kenny: Hey, Gary! What's the biggest prison?

Gary (again into cell phone): Leavenworth!

Kansas checks her camera, batteries, and laminated script of questions she's prepared to ask Joe and Kenny during this all-important final scene of her long-awaited documentary.

*****

Inside Joe's private cell, located on a minimum security cell block, serious Joe combs his gray hair and massages his temples as if he has a headache. He reaches inside his shirt pocket for his beeper.

At Guard Central Station, Bob checks Joe's cell on the monitor screen. He zooms in and sees Joe's extended hand is waving three fingers outside his cell, which means only one thing to his best friend and foster brother.

Not much later, Joe lies on his bed when he hears familiar footsteps and hustles to the front of his cell. Bob hands his friend three aspirin and a cup of water, which Joe swallows right away.

Bob: You know how many inmates we have in Bingham?

Joe: Nineteen hundred or so.

Bob: And how many private cells like yours are there in Bingham?

Joe shrugs and shakes his head that he doesn't know.

Bob: Guess.

Joe: Two hundred.

Bob: Sixteen. You know how old I was when I almost killed you for putting shaving cream on my pumpkin pie?

Joe (laughs): Sixteen.

They pause to just look at each other, two foster brothers who grew up together in Wichita under sometimes severe and desperate circumstances.

Bob: Tell me again how you hooked up with Bonnie.

Joe: I was in a bar and she asked me to dance. But there was no music playing on the jukebox. She gave me fifty cents and told me to play G-11. I didn't even look or care what song it was. I just put in the money and pressed G-11. We danced…and that was our song.

Bob: I start to tear up every time I hear that story. Is that in Joe's Story?

Joe (taps the side of his head): No, that's one good memory. I'm not letting that one out of here.

Bob: I'll be by when they get here. Get some rest.

Joe: Thanks, Bobby.

Bob walks away and Joe lies back down on his bed to think about the upcoming interview with Kenny.

*****

Later, Bob leads Kansas, Gary, and Kenny along a Bingham corridor to a private room where they can set up their camera equipment.

Bob (to Kansas): How long will it take you to set up?

39

Kansas: Not more than about five minutes.

Bob unlocks the door and the film crew enters the private visiting room furnished with a card table and four folding chairs. A ceiling-mounted surveillance camera is monitored by Guard Central Station.

Gary: How's the lighting?

Kansas sets up the camera on the tripod quickly.

Kansas: It'll have to do.

Director Kansas tells Kenny and Gary to sit on chairs close together at the card table's corner so she can frame them in her shot.

Kansas (looking into lens): I wish we had two cameras for this.

Gary (concerned): Will this work with one camera?

Kansas (directing Kenny): Stay right there. (To Gary)Take one of those other chairs and sit or stand behind me.

While Gary gets a chair to sit behind the camera, Kenny stretches and relaxes his body parts as if an actor preparing for a scene. Just then the door opens and only Joe enters. Joe smiles at the kids and hugs them before going over to Gary and shaking hands.

Joe: Mr. Fleming, I'm pleased to meet you again. I went to one of your Country Acres book signings in Garden City and bought your book.

Gary: So you're the one?

They both chuckle. Kansas gets Joe seated and checks the lens.

Kansas (behind the camera): That's good right there.

As Kenny breathes to relax with eyes closed, Kansas kneels down between them.

Kansas (to Joe): I'll ask the questions. I want you to just go into it. Kenny will be listening to you.

In Guard Central Station, Bob watches the monitor closely, along with Warden Ted and other guards and staff watching and listening to this last scene. They are all aware of the importance of the moment.

Kansas signals that she's starting the interview.

Kansas (off screen): My brother, Kenny Long, is here today in Bingham Correctional Facility to hear the truth from his father, Joe Long, who has served twelve years of his twenty-year mandatory sentence for the involuntary manslaughter of his wife, Bonnie, our mother. Yesterday, Kenny graduated from high school, and, as you know from watching this documentary, Joe Long is going to tell his son for the first time why he killed our mother.

Joe (on camera): Kenny, I just hated the way your mother ran around on me with her old boyfriend, Jerry Hope. He was my boss at Garden City Motors. I had been the service manager there for over five years. Your mom and I were drinking heavily that night when she turned mean and told me that Jerry Hope was your biological father.

Kenny appears unmoved by this news that Joe has been dreading to tell him.

Kansas (off screen): Joe, did you believe Bonnie when she told you Jerry was Kenny's biological father?

Joe: I believed her because before we were married she told me Jerry was also your biological father. I knew Jerry bought her the house, the new cars and expensive clothes.

41

Kenny: Dad?

Kansas and Joe are caught off guard.

Kenny: I heard it all. That night … I heard everything from my room. You thought I was asleep, but I wasn't. I don't care about Jerry Hope or any of that. You're my dad … and that's all I know.

Kenny and Joe are really connected now.

Kenny: I've always thought I could've stopped it by coming out of my room. But I didn't. I was afraid. All this time I've felt like it was my fault you were in here.

Kenny starts to sob with his head down in shame. Joe gets up and kneels beside Kenny and puts his arms around him. They sob together. Kansas is stunned by her brother's confession, and even Gary is moved by Kenny and Joe's raw emotion. Bob, Warden Ted, and the guards are glued to the monitor.

Joe: Kenny, you can't blame yourself for any of this. Your mom and I … this had nothing to do with you. Please understand that, son. It was all my fault.

Joe moves back to his seat facing Kenny.

Kenny (wiping his eyes): Dad, I always wondered why you agreed to twenty years without parole since the autopsy proved Mom died from a massive stroke.

Joe: I lost control. In my heart I know I caused it. And twenty years seemed right.

Kenny: Karen … Kansas … helped me see how I was hurting myself by not forgiving you and Mom. And she's right. But the hardest part has been forgiving myself. I'm still working on that. You have to forgive yourself, Dad. We both do.

As Joe cries, the camera stays on Joe as Kansas comes over and rubs his shoulders. Kenny kneels at Joe's feet and squeezes his hand.

Kansas (o. s.): Kenny's right, Dad. You have to forgive yourself.

Gary is impressed with this last scene.

Bob, Warden Ted, and the guards are moved by the scene they watched on the monitor in Guard Central Station.

Kansas is back behind the camera, and Joe and Kenny are in their seats.

Kansas (off screen): Joe, is there a good memory of Mom you can share?

Joe: What is this, Living Legacy?

The crew laughs.

Joe: Believe it or not, there are several good memories. One that comes to mind is when we were on our honeymoon in Denver. I went to get ice from the machine outside the room in the hall. It was late and I didn't think anybody was around, so I just went in my underwear. Well, I got locked out with no key, and your mother was in the tub in the bathroom with the fan running and couldn't hear me knocking. I had to go down to the lobby and get a key with all these people around and, of course, no ID. When I finally got back into the room and told your mother about it, she laughed so hard. (changes subject) The shrinks here want me to think of the good times. But they don't live here. After a while I had to remind myself what put me here. I spent too much time thinking of all the things she did and said to hurt me. I started blaming her for what got me here until I realized I had no right to cause her death. I didn't murder my wife. But I wanted to kill her that night.

43

Kenny: Temporary insanity.

Joe nods yes and appears contrite as Kansas ends the interview.

Kansas: Good!

Gary watches Joe and his kids hug. Soon, Bob enters the room and Joe nods goodbye to Gary. Bob escorts Joe out of the room.

Bob (to the visitors): Wait here for me.

Kansas and her brother pack up their equipment.

Gary (to Kansas): Maybe I can watch this again when we get back.

Kansas (smiles): Sure.

*****

 A bit later, Bob opens the security gate for the exiting film crew and hands Kenny a CD of Don Henley's Actual Miles, the same CD Joe had found in Jerry's car that fateful day.

Bob: Your dad wanted you to have this. He said you'd know "G-11."

Kenny knows the song.

*****

As Gary drives Traveller away from Bingham, he inserts the CD into the CD player. We hear the song "The Heart of the Matter" sung by Don Henley as Kenny and Kansas sit at the table with their backs against wall listening to the song known to both of them as "G-11"—their parents' song, which plays throughout:

{SERIES OF SHOTS}:

44

That night, Traveller and Shasta are parked and attached behind the Garden City motel.

At Traveller's table, Kansas and Gary watch the final scene on the laptop as:

Kenny lies on the bed in the dark Shasta trailer thinking about his last scene with Joe.

Later that night, Gary lies on his couch writing.

The next day, we see Kansas getting a copy made of her documentary disc as Gary is in the store aisle reading a legal form he needs.

In a bank, Kansas signs the legal form, which is then notarized by a banker. Gary gives Kansas a cashier's check for twenty thousand dollars, and Kansas hands Gary the original DVD disc and one copy of Joe's Story, as Gary requested.

Gary is dressed for business with a briefcase and laptop as he exits Traveller's back door at the back of the motel. He walks toward Garden City Motors across the street.

Gary opens the office door of "John Morgan, General Manager." JOHN MORGAN, 50 to 55 years old, greets Gary with a smile and handshake. Gary sits across the desk from Morgan explaining why he's there. Gary removes the laptop from its case and sees a family photo of John and Jane Morgan with his mother-in-law Mary Hope. John closes the blinds and turns off the lights after locking his office door for privacy.

John Morgan appears to enjoy the interview Kansas did with his wife and mother-in-law.

Later, John Morgan is visibly shaken at his desk as Gary puts away the laptop and turns on the lights. Gary hands John his proposal from his briefcase and exits the office as the music fades out.

45

Gary walks out of dealership and exhales markedly.

{END SERIES OF SHOTS}

*****

THAT NIGHT

Traveller is parked outside Gary's motel room at the Garden City Motel/Café. Gary soaks in the bathtub when a loud knock on his door startles him. He is concerned about who would be paying him a visit since he's just blackmailed a wealthy man. Gary puts on his bathrobe and goes to the peep-hole of his locked motel room door. Kenny and Kansas are standing outside the door and he lets them in. Kenny flops on the bed and lies on his side looking at Gary. Kansas takes a seat in the chair.

Kenny (to Gary): Did you sell it?

Gary: Too early. He watched it all. I gave him my proposal.

Kenny: How much money did you ask for?

Gary ignores the question.

Kenny: C'mon, Gary, you can tell us!

Gary won't talk about the details outlined in the proposal.

Kansas: If he doesn't buy it, will you market the DVD yourself?

Gary (pacing): Since I paid you twenty grand, I'll have to … and risk a lawsuit.

Kansas: It won't come to that. He'll buy.

Gary (stops pacing): Yeah? What makes you so sure?

46

Kansas: Because it's all true. It's a real story that will sell thousands just in this county.

Gary (changing the subject): Mr. Graduate, what are you going to do with twenty grand?

Kenny: I gave half of it to her.

Gary: That's mighty generous of you.

Kenny: We're starting an indie film company with my dad. He's setting us up with these stories inmates told him.

Kansas: Joe says we can get justice for the invisible people affected by crime, or bring justice to those who got away with one.

Gary: Like you two and Garden City Motors. Interesting.

Kenny (to Gary): You want in?

Gary: I might.

Kansas (smugly): It'll cost you twenty grand.

Gary (laughing): You're kidding.

Kansas: Ten to Kenny. Ten to me.

Gary (referring to Kenny): What's he going to do?

Kenny: I'll scout locations we need in order to set you and Kansas up to put it together. A "front man," Joe calls it.

Kansas: To do this right, Joe says we need a good front man.

Gary (to Kansas): Are you still going to shoot my signing tomorrow?

Kansas: Of course. In fact, tomorrow I'm buying a second camera to use for your signing and the projects Joe's lined up.

Gary (to Kenny): I'll need your help tomorrow.

Kenny: On one condition:

*****

Later, in Traveller's bathroom, Kenny looks up at the wedged toothpick near the crank of the blowing fan while getting stoned with Gary in close quarters.

Kenny: Any guy who can use a toothpick to solve a problem must be one creative dude.

Gary puts away the stash and pipe in the bathroom cabinet, turns off the fan, removes the toothpick and cranks shut the overhead fan.

Kenny: What are you going to talk about at your gig tomorrow?

Gary (smiles at the toothpick in his hand): Being creative.

Kenny smiles at Gary.

*****

NEXT DAY

Kenny stacks twenty cases of Gary's books on a flatbed cart from Traveller's open back door while parked in front of Country Acres Retirement Home.

Inside the Country Acres large dining room, Gary is dressed sharp in jeans, shirt and tie. His sports jacked is draped over a chair as he tests the microphone at the podium on the portable stage in front of 100 empty folding chairs with a middle aisle. The chairs are spaced for seniors—lots of room. A table with two chairs is near the podium. Gary goes to the table, opens his laptop, and checks again for that important message he hopes to get from John Morgan. The deadline for Gary's proposal was before his signing began at Country Acres. On the laptop screen there are no messages … still.

Hearing Kenny approaching with the cart down the middle aisle, Gary reaches into his jacket pocket and places a box cutter on the table. Kansas sets up her old camera on a tripod near the stage for Kenny; her new camera is on a tripod along the wall.

Gary (points for Kenny): Make sure you open all the cases now with that box cutter! Stack the books by title in front on the floor and leave some space between each title!

Kenny (mumbling): No problem, boss man.

Kansas (to Gary): Any news yet?

Gary checks his laptop screen once more and shakes his head no. He puts on his sports jacket hoping his proposal is accepted … and soon.

*****

Later, the Country Acres parking lot is full of vehicles. Traveller has been moved and parked near Kansas's station wagon at the back of the parking lot.

The dining room now has a full house seated on folding chairs. The AUDIENCE watches the COUNTRY ACRES ADMINISTRATOR, a 55- to 60-year-old Caucasian woman, walk to the podium as Kenny is behind the camera close to the podium. Kansas is behind the new camera along the wall. Just then Gary sees Jane Morgan and Mary Hope in the audience. He checks his laptop one last time and he sees he has a new message. He reads one-word message: "DONE". Gary quickly types on his keyboard.

Administrator (off screen into the mic): Welcome to our fifteenth annual book signing and fundraiser with indie author, G. K. Fleming!

During the applause Gary sits stunned staring at the laptop screen that shows $100,000.00 has been deposited in his bank account. Kansas and Kenny know something's up.

Administrator: It's always an interesting time with our favorite author here at Country Acres. (pointing to books) Let's sell lots of books and now welcome Mr. Fleming to Garden City!

Applause brings stunned and thrilled Gary to the podium.

Gary: Thanks for coming! I actually have fantastic news. I'm not going to try to sell you my books today.

Kenny and Kansas are confused until Gary reaches into his coat pocket and removes a check he wrote out earlier.

Gary (emotional): Thanks to some invisible law of attraction and the good folks at Garden City Motors, every last book in my inventory—one thousand books—has been bought. And here is a check for five thousand dollars made out to Country Acres!

The shocked administrator starts the applause. Gary gives her the check, and we see the confused Garden City women—Mary Hope and her daughter Jane Morgan—applauding and smiling, yet unaware of this gift to Country Acres.

Gary: So come on up here a row at a time while Kenny and I give you as many books as you can carry!

Gary goes down to the audience line where he and Kenny load each person with ten books.

Gary (to audience): No, I can't sign books! There's too many!

*****

Later, the Country Acres lot is nearly empty as Kenny and Gary each carry ten flattened cardboard boxes to the dumpster, and

50

Kansas carries her equipment to her station wagon parked near Traveller.

Kenny: You got rid of every last book. How do you feel right now?

Gary: Lighter.

Kenny: Kansas says you're in.

Gary: That's right. When do we see Joe?

Kenny: Soon. After we move out of the motel.

They reach the dumpster and unload the boxes, then start walking back to the motel.

Gary: Kenny, there's one thing you and your sister have to do now:

*****

Later, on the Garden City Motors used car lot, Kenny and Kansas walk between rows of used cars. Kansas stops to inspect a red 2012 Jeep Cherokee she likes.

Kansas (to Kenny): Are you sure we're supposed to be here?

Kenny's attention is on a black 2003 Mustang.

John Morgan (off screen): Is this your trade-in?

Kansas and Kenny turn to see the smiling face of John Morgan standing beside the old station wagon. Kansas gives the general manager a wincing affirmative nod.

*****

Later, behind the motel, Gary is filling Traveller's water tank with a hose as a red Jeep and black Mustang drive over to him and park. Kansas and Kenny walk over to Gary.

Gary: You get your titles?

They both nod yes, smiling at the man who arranged this.

Gary: We better get Shasta hooked up to Traveller. I suggest you get the vehicles plated and registered here Monday morning while you can still use this address.

Kansas (smiling): I think that's a good idea.

Gary: So … any idea what Joe has for us?

*****

Meanwhile, in the Bingham dining hall, Joe stands in the breakfast line as correctional officer Bob searches for and finds seated inmate Larry Welck, a 35- to 40-year-old Caucasian inmate, having breakfast at a table. Two other inmates are seated across from Welck. Bob stands behind Welck and the other two inmates get up and leave with their trays. Joe sits down with his tray across from Welck. Bob slips a folded piece of paper into Welck's shirt pocket and stands behind Welck.

Joe: Larry, you read that when you get back to your crib. If you agree, sign it and Bob will pick it up after lights out. (sips coffee) You'll be signing over all rights to your story to me.

Joe gets up from the table.

Welck: And what exactly do I get out of this?

Joe bends down to pick up his tray from the table and holds there.

Joe (intensely into Welck's eyes): You get your only chance to help your mother … and make Jimmy pay.

52

Welck's eyes go to the tray and stay there as Joe stands up with his tray.

Joe: Sign that before lights out, or I go on to the next guy ... and you get to keep your story.

Joe leaves and Bob follows him out of the dining hall.

At the prison phone bank area for inmates Joe dials a phone number. Kansas answers her cell phone while packing a suitcase on her bed.

Kansas (on cell phone): Hey!

Joe (o. s. on phone): Is the writer in?

Kansas: Yes! He did it, Joe! He really did it!

Bob signals to Joe to wrap it up. Joe nods to Bob.

Kansas: Are you ready for us?

Joe: I've been ready a long time. Look, I'm over my phone time this month. I have to go. Love you.

Kansas (o. s. on phone): Love you.

Joe hangs up the phone and smiles at Bob.

Joe: He's in.

Bob and Joe celebrate with a discreet handshake.

*****

Joe has just returned to his cell. He walks over to his desk and finds Gary's book Indie Writer: How To Publish And Market Your Book The Hard Way. Joe turns the book over to the back cover and smiles at Gary's photo standing in front of Traveller's vehicle lettering, Don't Read My Books. We get the feeling Joe has pulled

53

off something he's been planning for a long time as Don Henley singing "The Heart of the Matter" begins and plays throughout:

{SERIES OF SHOTS}:

Kansas carries clothes into Shasta that's now hooked up to Traveller. Kenny is on his back connecting wiring for the brake and signal lights which Gary sees blinking.

Kansas and Kenny put new license plates on their new vehicles.

Gary has writer's block at a window table in the motel's café.

Traveller's overhead bathroom fan cover opens and the fan comes on.

Gary writes up a storm while lying with one leg elevated on Traveller's couch.

Garden City Motel/Café employees wave goodbye to the caravan leaving the parking lot with Traveller leading the way pulling Shasta. Kansas follows in her packed red Jeep with Kenny behind her in his black Mustang.

The song fades out as the caravan rolls east on the highway.

{END SERIES OF SHOTS}

End of Pilot

Episode 2:

Secret Fire

On the vast Bingham Prison parking lot, an unmarked black prison van with tinted glass all around parks in front of Traveller as if blocking its way. The red Jeep and black Mustang are parked by Traveller.

Inside Traveller, Gary, Kansas and Kenny are seated at the table having coffee, and are surprised when they see uniformed Bob open the side door of the van and out steps handcuffed Joe carrying a file folder. Bob waits outside Traveller.

> Joe: Anybody home?

> Gary: Come in!

Joe and Gary shake hands before Joe hugs Kenny and Kansas.

> Kenny: What are you doing here?

Bob stands near Traveller's back door listening.

> Joe: A little trade I made with Warden Ted for some consulting work.

Joe sits on couch with Gary. Kansas and Kenny sit at the table; the crew knows their leader has arrived.

> Kansas: Did you see the vehicles Gary got us?

Joe: I wonder who got the Mustang! (beat) They don't give me much time so I'll cut to the chase. (to Gary) I am so impressed with the job you did and so glad you joined our team. We couldn't do this without you. (beat) Gary, did you give Kenny and Kansas their ten grand each?

Gary: Not yet.

Joe: Please do that now.

Gary fumbles for his checkbook and writes out checks fast after changing seats with Kenny.

Joe: I have to talk fast, so as soon as Gary is finished...

Gary: Kansas, who do I make your check out to?

Kansas (awkward): Karen Long.

Bob heard that and shakes his head in disgust while Joe smiles at his adopted daughter who has always called him *Joe*. Gary hands checks to a grateful Kenny and Kansas.

Joe: Here's the way we roll. I'm the director. You're the crew. I make the big decisions, including how much to charge the target for the documentary. Gary, how much did you get from Garden City Motors?

Gary: A hundred grand.

Joe: I would've gotten three times that much.

Gary is beside himself after hearing that.

Joe: From now on, I decide how much the documentary is worth.

Gary nods in agreement.

56

Joe: The money is divided into four shares. Kansas and Kenny split a share. Gary, you get two shares because you manage the crew and take the biggest risk. Only you will pitch the target, because you own the rights to every documentary. The fourth share goes to whomever the inmate designates. It may go to a relative or friend of the inmate, or whomever he wants the share to go to. The job isn't done until all shares are paid. The inmate and I don't get paid.

Bob (off screen): Me, neither!

Gary: So each of us covers our own expenses?

Joe: Expenses are paid equally by shares. So Gary, you pay half the expenses. (to crew) I suggest after this case you all rent a house together near here, somewhere you can park all your vehicles and have a home base to work from.

Gary: This is my home.

Joe: That's fine, Gary, but you can't all live and work out of here to save money. You need a home base to rest. You need your own space.

Kenny: That's cool. Maybe we can get a furnished house.

Kansas: Yeah, it would be nice to have my own bathroom.

Handcuffed Joe stands and drops his file folder titled *Secret Fire* onto the table.

Joe: Everything I know about that case is in that folder. (to Gary) As you did in Garden City, it's your job to put it all together, to write and direct a story that's easy to sell to the target.

Before Joe exits Traveller:

Joe (to Kenny and Kansas): Can I speak to you two in private?

57

Outside, in the Bingham parking lot, Joe and his kids stand by their new vehicles with Bob nearby.

Joe: Can you two work with Gary?

Kansas and Kenny nod yes.

Joe (softens): I want you to know that all this is for you. I can't make up for what I did to your lives. This is all I have to keep us together. Study that file and help Gary create a good documentary we can sell to the target or public, whichever is necessary.

After quick hugs, Bob escorts Joe into the prison van's side door and they watch the van drive back into prison as:

Back inside Traveller, Gary sees something disturbing in the *Secret Fire* file that Joe gave him.

Later, at a modern rest area, the crew's caravan is parked with idling 18-wheelers. The crew brainstorms "Secret Fire" file in Traveller as Kenny gets a soda from the fridge.

Gary (cynical to Kenny): Need an aspirin?

Kenny and Kansas laugh at Gary's humor.

Gary: Okay, let's sum up what we know from the file. Larry Welck and Jimmy Boyle were just out of high school. They've never been in trouble. They were star football players at Abilene High.

Kenny: Jimmy Boyle had a football scholarship at Kansas State.

Gary: Right. And Jimmy Boyle the wide receiver owes his quarterback big time.

Kansas: So Boyle is our target.

Gary nods yes.

Kenny: A best friend does not let this go on for sixteen years.

Kansas: Yeah, what a lousy deal for dumb-luck Larry.

Gary: We have to go to Abilene.

Kansas (on iPad): It's a ninety-minute drive from here. I'd like to get a nice RV park where I could shower and do laundry.

Gary: Find an RV park in Abilene on that thing there.

Kansas: It's an iPad.

*****

Later that night, Traveller is plugged in with waste hose connected to sewer in nice RV campsite. Kenny's Mustang is parked behind Shasta as Jeep arrives and parks behind Mustang. Kenny and Kansas carry groceries to Traveller's porch light where the back step is down.

Gary is stoned and writing up a storm on Traveller's couch with one leg elevated.

Kenny: Food's here!

Gary gets up and opens screen door for them to enter. Kenny sees and HEARS bathroom fan running. Gary puts groceries away while Kansas and Kenny wait at table.

Gary: Any ideas from you two?

As Kansas logs on to her laptop Kenny discreetly points to his lips as if he's asking Gary if he can use his pipe. Gary nods yes and Kenny hustles into bathroom.

Kansas (on laptop): We could interview their football coach first.

Gary: I was thinking that, too. Nobody knows Secret Fire like Coach Roan.

Kenny (from bathroom): Can I go with you to see Coach Roan?

Gary: You have to go. You're the second cameraman. (to Kansas) Can you help me with a list of interview questions for the coach?

Kansas: There's only one question to ask Coach Roan.

Gary: What's that?

*****

NEXT DAY

Kansas and Kenny are behind cameras as Gary interviews middle-aged Caucasian, COACH ROAN at his desk in his office.

Gary (on camera): Coach, what was "Secret Fire?"

Coach smiles while recalling fondly:

Coach Roan: Two boys grew up in the same Abilene neighborhood. One was a quarterback -

Gary: Larry Welck.

Coach Roan: That's right. And Jimmy Boyle was a wide out. They practiced this forty-yard fly pattern they named "Secret Fire". Larry would lay out Jimmy with a circus catch that only Jimmy

60

could catch. It won us several games and got Jimmy a full ride at Wichita State. Those young men were a joy to coach.

Gary: Larry Welck didn't get to go to college. He went to Bingham Prison. What would you say to Larry now?

Coach Roan: I went to Bingham to visit Larry a few times over the years. I heard he could get out soon. I told Larry to make the best of his time, stay in shape, read books, and stay out of trouble.

Gary: Thank you, Coach, for your time. (to camera) I can't help but wonder what Jimmy Boyle would say to his old quarterback right now. Would he give Larry a job at Boyle's Construction, Jimmy's construction company in Abilene, since Boyle's best friend and quarterback has been incarcerated for sixteen years for a crime he didn't do alone?

Coach Roan thinks the interview is over. The crew knows the cameras are still on and picking up any dialog as planned by Gary.

Coach Roan (to Gary): What is this about Larry not acting alone?

Gary (smiling at coach): You will have to buy the DVD to find out.

Coach Roan: You bet I will.

Gary: I hope to get it placed in several Abilene retailers. It should sell big in Abilene.

Coach Roan: I know it will.

* * * * *

Later, outside at Boyle Construction in Abilene, JIMMY BOYLE, 34, Caucasian general contractor, gives instructions to his CONSTRUCTION CREW returning from job site. He breaks away from his crew to answer his cell phone.

Jimmy Boyle (on cell phone): Boyle Construction, this is Jimmy. Hey, Coach! What's up?

Jimmy does not like what he hears from Coach Roan.

Jimmy Boyle (on phone): Is that right? (gets notepad & pen) Who's this writer now?

Jimmy scribbles down G. K. Fleming. At his office desk, Jimmy looks at Gary's web page on laptop screen and sees that all his books are out of print. He clicks on orange letters on tab "Secret Fire" and reads Gary's web site:

Jimmy Boyle (reads web site)*: Larry Welck has served nearly sixteen years in Bingham Maximum Security Prison for a crime he didn't do alone. How can a man go to prison for the prime years of his life and allow his accomplice to remain free all that time? DVD coming soon to Abilene retailers.*

Jimmy turns off his computer and thinks about his next move.

*****

At RV campsite the caravan is parked at one site. Traveller's door is open and his back step is down.

Inside Traveller, Gary sits across the table from Kansas and Kenny while having dinner together and discussing the case.

Gary: I'll bet Boyle's heard about us by now. (to Kansas) Can you text Bob?

Kansas nods yes while eating.

Kenny: Any ideas, Gary?

Gary: Yeah … if Joe approves it.

Kansas (ready to text): What do you want me to text?

*****

Bachelor Bob enters his kitchen from back yard patio with grilled steak on platter in middle-class neighborhood. Bob sees he has a text message on his cell phone on the counter. He reads text message with keen interest.

*****

That night, Jimmy Boyle sits on a bar stool in a quiet bar staring at his can of beer in hand on top of the bar.

{BOYLE'S FLASHBACK}:

It's winter in 1999 when YOUNG WELCK, 18, parks his 88 Olds 4-door as YOUNG BOYLE, 18, riding shotgun, points to where Larry Welck should park as if this is Jimmy Boyle's idea. Larry parks behind a bus stop with convenience store behind them on the passenger side of car. Boyle puts on a ski mask.

     Young Welck: Jimmy, think about this: You're going to steal a six-pack of beer and risk losing your full ride at Kansas State?

     Young Boyle: They sure as hell won't sell it to me. (opens door) Leave it running. I'll be back quick with a few cold ones. Larry, listen to me. Nobody gets hurt or goes to jail for a few lousy beers.

Welck can only watch his friend and favorite wide receiver hustle into the store via his rear passenger-side window, unaware of a city bus stopping in front of him and parking at a bus stop.

Inside the convenience store, Boyle is at beer cooler, grabs six-pack and hustles out of store with no clerk at register. Boyle runs with beer toward car as if he's carrying a football. Boyle dives onto back seat with Welck unaware HOMELESS MAN is crossing street in front of his car.

63

Young Boyle (flat on back seat): Secret Fire! Secret Fire!!

Welck floors the accelerator without looking ahead and hits a
homeless man, killing him. Boyle doesn't know what's happened
because he's on the back seat.

Young Boyle: GO!

The parked city BUS DRIVER sees only Welck in his side-view
mirror as he watches Welck speed away, leaving scene of accident.
The bus driver gets on his phone.

Welck turns the corner, pulls over and parks with Boyle still down
on the back seat.

Young Welck: You can get out. I have to go back. You don't
have to be a part of this.

Young Boyle: Are you crazy? Just GO! SECRET FIRE!

Soon, young Boyle leaves his coat, ski mask, and the stolen beer on
the floor of the back seat as emergency vehicles approach. That's
when Boyle bolts from the car and vanishes into the darkness.

{END OF BOYLE'S FLASHBACK}

Back at the bar on the barstool, Boyle pushes his beer away and
leaves the bar.

*****

NEXT DAY

Joe sits at his private, shaded table; he's writing alone on the
Bingham prison grounds.

Joe (voice over writing): *Larry Welck told me that Jimmy
Boyle's coat, ski mask and beer, caught on the store's surveillance
camera, made it easy for Larry to take the fall alone when police*

*found those same items on his back seat. I heard from Warden Ted
a while back that he thought Larry would've been out for vehicular
manslaughter after seven years, except the petty larceny before the
accident gave him a minimum of sixteen years. Jimmy did visit
Larry a few times over the first few years when Jimmy was doing
well on his football scholarship at Kansas State. The visits got
further apart and Boyle never did make good on his promise to help
Larry's mother over the years. Now it's time for Jimmy Boyle to
pay for his freedom all these years.*

Joe closes his notebook as Warden Ted approaches. They both light
a cigarette as Warden Ted sits across from Joe's private writing
space that the warden gave him over the years.

Warden Ted: I heard the board is voting to ban smoking in all
the facilities.

Joe: That's no good.

Warden Ted: By now the entire prison staff has seen your last
scene with Kenny. Karen did a good job raising him for you.

Joe: Karen changed her name to Kansas.

Warden Ted: That's interesting.

Joe: I wanted to thank you again for letting me visit my kids in
the parking lot. I got to see their new vehicles.

Warden Ted: Joe, if it was up to me ... (leans forward) ... I'd let
you walk out of here tomorrow. The good work you do for inmates
here is spreading. Today I had two of our Texas wardens call me,
asking me about you. They want to interview you about what you
do here. Joe, I'm starting to see how this could be a positive thing
for all penal facilities, not just here at Bingham.

Joe: I have a big favor I'd like to ask of you, Warden. Please hear me out. And know right up front that it's not going to cost your prison a dime.

Warden Ted listens to Joe's MUTED words.

*****

That night, at the crew's RV campground campsite, the lights are on inside Traveller and Shasta, the travel trailer where Kenny and Kansas sleep. Shasta is still connected to Traveller. Now the crew is inside Traveller as Gary trips over Kenny's big feet.

Kansas: I think Joe was right. We should get our own space. Like a furnished house.

Kenny: That would be so sweet.

Gary (takes charge): Wait a minute. Until we see how Secret Fire works out, we hold tight and live in tight quarters.

Kansas: What's your plan with Boyle?

Gary (to Kenny): Now's the time our front man visits the target.

Kenny: Just put me in the game, Coach.

Gary (to Kenny): I'll have a short script for you ready in the morning.

Kenny: Breakfast on the crew manager?

Gary smiles at Kenny.

Kenny: Sweet. I've got to grab a shower.

Kenny leaves Traveller.

Kansas: I saw this cool house for rent in the country. Want to go look?

Gary: Ask me again when you go.

Kansas: Okay. (beat) I'm going to read myself to sleep.

Gary: What are you reading?

Kansas: This book I bought on Amazon. I can't remember the title.

*****

Later, in Shasta, Kansas reads a book in bed. We see the cover of a paperback book by G. K. Fleming.

*****

SERIES OF SHOTS:

Later, inside Traveller, Gary writes on the couch under a light with his leg elevated.

Next day, in the Bingham dining hall, Bob picks up a folded note from the table where Joe and Larry Welck are having a chat during breakfast. Bob texts note to:

The crew is having breakfast at a window table in a restaurant when Kansas shows text from Bob to Gary.

Later, Gary walks around the RV park thinking about the case.

END SERIES OF SHOTS

*****

That day, Kenny parks his Mustang across the street from the Boyle Construction office. Boyle's truck is parked near the entrance to his office.

Kenny enters Boyle's office and walks up to the contractor seated behind his desk.

Kenny: Mr. Boyle?

Kenny hands Boyle a folded release form.

Kenny: I represent G. K. Fleming, the independent filmmaker. He'll be contacting you soon regarding interviewing you for his documentary, *Secret Fire*.

Boyle watches Kenny leave his office.

*****

NEXT DAY

Larry Welck mops the floor on work detail on his cell block when Bob walks over to him.

Bob: Welck, you have a visitor.

Welck is surprised, although Joe has prepared Welck for this particular visitor.

Welck is escorted into the private visiting area by Bob. Jimmy Boyle is seated on the other side of the glass.

Jimmy Boyle: I hear you're getting out soon.

Welck doesn't respond.

Jimmy Boyle: Coach called me. He said he was interviewed by this writer making this documentary, *Secret Fire*. Coach says it proves you weren't alone that night.

Welck is quiet.

Jimmy Boyle (discreetly): What's this about, Larry? You were the one who decided to take this on yourself. What do you want from me? A job when you get out? You got it.

Larry Welck: I don't want a job from you.

Jimmy Boyle: What do you want?

Larry Welck: Justice. For sixteen years I'm in here and you're out there doing nothing for my mother. All these years you've been telling me you'll help her out. What was that, Jimmy … lip service?

Jimmy Boyle (leans closer to glass): Your mother would never take money from me or let me do anything for her. She'd only be suspicious.

Larry Welck: That's bull. You could've replaced her roof, added on a deck, remodeled her kitchen. (beat) Now Mr. Fleming will help my mother.

Jimmy Boyle: You can't prove I was there.

Larry stands up

Larry Welck: Like Mr. Fleming says: I don't have to prove you were there. You'll have to convince everybody you weren't.

Larry walks away, leaving Boyle frustrated and into his head.

*****

Joe is alone writing at his private table on the prison grounds when Bob escorts Larry Welck over to Joe's table.

Joe: Sit down, Larry.

Welck sits across from Joe. Bob waits nearby.

Joe: What did Boyle say?

Larry Welck: He's no good. He says I can't prove he was there that night.

Joe (taking notes): What did you say to that?

Larry Welck: I told him what you told me to say.

Joe nods positively.

Joe: Do you think he'll sit for an interview with Mr. Fleming?

Larry Welck: No way.

Joe and Bob know each other so well that Bob calls Guard Central with his digital pager and dials a code number to let them know he wants an officer to escort an inmate back to his cell.

Bob: Larry, go wait by that door, please.

Larry walks away as an OFFICER appears and escorts Larry away.

Bob: You still want Mr. Fleming to go see Jimmy Boyle?

Joe: Yeah. Let's just see what Mr. Fleming can come up with.

Bob: You want the man to earn his money.

Joe: I want to see what a creative man can produce out there.

Bob: What about that favor the warden gave you?

Joe: That favor will cost Mr. Fleming a share if we have to use that favor. Let's just see what this writer comes up with.

*****

SERIES OF SHOTS:

Kansas parks her Jeep in front of a modest Abilene house. Gary and Kenny get out of the Jeep with Kansas and carry their camera equipment up to front door where smiling widow, MRS. WELCK, 55-60, holds open her front door as if she's been expecting them.

We see a MUTED interview at the kitchen table between Gary and Mrs. Welck with Kenny and Kansas behind their cameras. Her son's high school graduation picture is on the kitchen table.

Inside Traveller that night, Kansas edits on her laptop at the table under a light while getting Gary and Kenny's MUTED but animated feedback.

In an office supply store, Kansas makes a copy of her DVD and hands the copy to Gary.

END SERIES OF SHOTS.

*****

NEXT DAY

From Kenny's parked Mustang, Kenny watches Jimmy Boyle arrive in his truck and walk into his office.

Boyle is seated at his desk looking at a computer screen when Kenny enters Boyle's office carrying a DVD. Boyle is not happy to see this errand boy for that writer.

Kenny (offers disc): Mr. Fleming wants you to see this.

Boyle takes the disc.

Kenny: Did you sign the release form?

Jimmy Boyle (haughty): No, I didn't. I thought I'd show it to my lawyer first.

Kenny: I suggest you show your lawyer that DVD too.

Kenny leaves the office. Boyle plays the DVD right away. On the computer screen is Mrs. Welck pleading for Jimmy's help:

Mrs. Welck (on screen): *Jimmy, you were Larry's best friend. I'm told by Mr. Fleming that you alone have information that can help get Larry released. The parole board could release Larry soon. Please be there, Jimmy. Whatever it is that you know, Mr. Fleming is going to put it on a DVD and sell it all over Abilene, if that's what it takes to get Larry released. Please do the right thing. I miss my son.*

Boyle turns off the computer and thinks about his dilemma.

*****

Later, in Bingham's Family Visiting Area, Kansas and Gary see Joe walking toward their table. It's all business when Joe sits across from them.

Joe: What's new?

Gary: Kenny just delivered to Boyle my interview with Welck's mother, where she pleads with Boyle to show up and testify at Welck's upcoming parole hearing.

Joe (confused): There's no hearing scheduled.

Gary: I know.

Joe thinks about where Gary is going with this.

Joe (thinking out loud): Interesting. This puts Mrs. Welck in the picture, causing potential problems for Boyle if he doesn't show for a parole hearing. But there is no hearing for Welck scheduled.

Gary: Could there be?

Joe: The parole board meets once a month in Wichita. (to Gary) I should tell you a couple things I didn't cover. If a case involves the prison or their staff, it costs you one of your two shares. Warden Ted let me come out to your RV because he wants me to do consulting work for other prisons. I agreed to and asked the warden if he would allow Bob to escort Welck out of here for a couple hours to meet with Boyle. (to Kansas) I thought you could record their conversation and we'd have some leverage to close the deal with Boyle.

Gary: I like that. Boyle will think Welck is out of prison. Losing a share would be worth it to me.

Joe (to Kansas): Get the right mic and camera you need that will incriminate Boyle, and we have a good shot at closing him fast. (to both) Any equipment you buy comes out of the share that Gary loses.

Gary: Who do I give the balance of my lost share to?

Joe: I'll let you know.

Kansas: We decided we want to get our own place.

Joe: I've been thinking about that. The warden says that these consulting gigs will mean I get to do some traveling.

Gary: Really?

Joe nods yes.

Kansas: So we'd travel, too?

Joe: Most of the best cases are out of Kansas.

Gary: What do you mean by "best"?

Joe: Easy.

Gary (nods in agreement): Easy is good.

Joe: So get a house with a short-term lease.

Gary: I might just live in Traveller.

Joe (to Gary): But stay close.

Gary indicates that he will.

Joe: So, like with my last scene with Kenny in *Joe's Story*, create one good last scene in *Secret Fire* and have Kansas text the details.

Both Kansas and Gary nod that they will.

Joe (intensely): And know that we won't close every file with a sale. Some will get away from us. My job is to give you a good shot that's clean.

They get up from the table when Joe stands. Joe hugs Kansas and shakes hands with Gary.

Joe (handshaking): Gary, thanks for your good work.

*****

Meanwhile, inside a CD store, Kenny browses through Grateful Dead CDs near long-haired HIPPIE KID, 18-20, who wears a Grateful Dead T-shirt.

Kenny (to hippie): I love Grateful Dead.

The kid moves away from Kenny but Kenny follows him.

Kenny (discreetly to kid): Hey, man...I just moved here and need to get hooked up.

*****

A bit later, inside a van, the hippie kid lights a bong for Kenny in the cargo area of van as Grateful Dead MUSIC faintly plays from van's stereo. After Kenny exhales:

Kenny (smiles): Pretty smooth.

Hippie Kid: A quarter-ounce of my stash is eighty bucks.

Kenny: This stuff?

Kenny smiles.

*****

SERIES OF SHOTS:

At the RV campsite that night, Kenny's Mustang is gone. The lights are on inside Traveller.

In Traveller, Gary and Kansas eat at the table as Kansas points out different mic equipment on the laptop screen.

In mall game room we see Kenny is stoned wearing sunglasses while playing a pinball machine with earbud inserted from his iPod.

Later that night, Gary writes on Traveller's couch.

In Shasta trailer, Kansas reads in bed, resisting the urge to call Kenny.

END SERIES OF SHOTS

*****

Later that night, the Shasta trailer is dark when tired Kenny enters quietly, carrying his new futon bed. Kansas flips on her bedside light.

Kansas: Little late, isn't it?

Kenny positions the futon on the floor of the dinky trailer and falls onto it.

Kansas: Where did you get that?

Kenny: Abilene Mall.

Kansas: Is it comfortable?

Kenny: Uh-huh.

After Kansas turns off her bedside light:

Kansas: We saw Joe today.

Kenny: Yeah?

Kansas: I told him we want our own place.

Kenny: And?

Kansas: He said we should get a place near Wichita. And we might get to travel with him.

Kenny: Sweet. It's like Dad has this great job in prison that he created and we get paid for.

Kansas: Where did you go tonight?

Kenny: I went to the mall, played some pinball, bought this bed for my sore back. (beat) Bought some good weed.

Kenny waits for his sister to say something maternal, but she doesn't. What Kenny said triggers an old memory for Kansas.

{KANSAS'S FLASHBACK}:

It's night at a Venice Beach coffeehouse in 2003. Karen is 17; she smokes a cigarette on break with co-worker, STONER BRUCE, 22-25, blonde surfer and nice guy.

Stoner Bruce: I scored some good weed today and got this.

Bruce shows Karen his new tattoo of a red devil with horns and pitchfork on his forearm.

Karen: That's nice. Who did that?

Stoner Bruce: I did.

Karen (impressed): You're a tattoo artist!

Bruce's laugh is impish, but safe-sounding to Karen.

Karen: Don't you have to be licensed to do that?

Stoner Bruce: Yeah, if you have a shop. My brother owns Gabe's Flesh Art.

Karen: Oh yeah, I've seen that place. How much would a tattoo like that cost?

Stoner Bruce (smiling): For you?

Kansas smiles back.

*****

Later that night after work, Karen smokes a bowl in Bruce's studio apartment while Bruce finishes putting red-lettered tattoo of "Kansas" on Karen's butt cheek.

Stoner Bruce: Does this mean I can call you Kansas?

Karen (thinking): Yeah. That's my new name.

{END OF KANSAS'S FLASHBACK}

Back in Shasta, Kansas HEARS her brother sleeping and goes to sleep as:

*****

The lights are on in Traveller as Gary paces the aisle thinking about this last scene in *Secret Fire* that could close this case fast without problems.

*****

Next morning, the crew is having breakfast in a café booth. Kansas and Kenny sit across from haggard Gary, who's frustrated from brainstorming dead-end ideas all night.

Kansas (to Gary): I saw your light on late last night.

Gary: I kept losing the last scene.

Kenny: So nothing yet?

Gary: Nothing real solid. I keep coming up with Welck meeting Boyle somewhere that doesn't work.

Kansas (explains to Kenny): Joe told us that he could get Welck released for a couple hours so Boyle would believe he was out.

Kenny: Really? (eating) Then my idea could work.

Gary (curious): What idea?

Kenny: Well, yesterday I was playing pinball after I delivered the DVD to Boyle.

Kansas: While stoned.

Kenny laughs.

Kenny: Anyway, I was thinking how "Secret Fire" is this football play that made these guys famous around here. (to Gary)

78

What if they met on the same field where they made a name for themselves?

Gary (imagining): Yeah. (likes idea) What if they did?

Kenny: Gary, if you use my idea can I have some of your share?

Gary: I already lose a share if we get Joe's help from inside.

Kansas (to Kenny): Joe told us that yesterday.

Gary (to Kenny): But I will pay your first month's rent if we use your idea.

Kenny: Sweet.

*****

Later, inside an electronics store, Kansas picks out an expensive mic and telescopic lens for the upcoming scene with Welck and Boyle that Gary buys with a debit card.

*****

At dusk, at the Abilene high school football field, Kenny and Gary walk down the middle of the field having a conversation that is heard by Karen, who's hidden under the visiting team's bleachers.

Under the bleachers, Karen can see and HEAR Gary and Kenny with the new lens and mic:

Gary (on mic): Can we shoot this at night?

Kenny (on mic): We'll ask Kansas. (beat) We forgot something, Gary.

Gary (on mic): What?

SERIES OF SHOTS:

In a sporting goods store, Kenny picks out a football and Gary pays for it.

In Traveller at night, Gary writes on the couch under an overhead light.

In Traveller, the next day, Kansas sends text from Gary's script.

In Guard Central Station, Bob reads text from Kansas.

In Bingham dining hall, Bob places folded note on table where Joe eats alone. Joe puts folded note into his shirt pocket.

Back in his private cell, Joe reads unseen note and responds with one-word note given to Bob waiting outside his cell.

Back to Traveller, the crew reads the text message from Joe: "GO".

END SERIES OF SHOTS

*****

It's early evening as Joe smokes at his private writing table while seated across from Larry Welck. Bob, standing nearby, dials a number on his cell phone and hands the phone to Welck, who reads from a script:

Larry Welck (on cell phone): Jimmy, I'm out. Yeah! Mr. Fleming and Warden Ted arranged a meeting with the parole board and they released me. Yeah. I'm in Abilene. Look, Jimmy, before I close this documentary deal with Mr. Fleming, I want to talk to you. Tonight. Yeah, I can't sleep anyway. Meet me at Abilene Field at midnight. Yeah. We can talk there. I've got my mom's car. Okay. Bye.

Bob takes back his phone and wipes it off on his sleeve.

Larry Welck (to Joe): He'll be there. I think I woke him up.

Joe: That's the idea.

Bob sends a text to Kansas that reads: "12 tonight". Then Bob makes another quick call we don't hear. Welck gets up from the table and picks up his bag full of clothes.

Larry Welck (to Joe): I wish you could ride along.

Joe: This is your thing, Larry. Just get him to talk about what he did and didn't do. Follow your script.

Larry Welck: Thanks for this, Joe. This is good work you do.

Bob takes the bag from Welck when an unmarked black transportation van with tinted windows all around drives up and parks leaving the engine running. The guard driver waits nearby as Bob puts the bag in the van, handcuffs Welck, helps Welck onto the back passenger seat behind a security cage before putting leg irons on his prisoner.

Bob (to guard driver): Escort Mr. Long back to his cell.

Joe watches Bob get behind the wheel of the van and drive out of the facility.

*****

Meanwhile, Jimmy Boyle hangs his head in a running shower after getting that phone call from his old quarterback.

{BOYLE'S FLASHBACK}:

In Bingham private visiting area, Young Boyle, 20, sits behind glass as Young Welck takes a seat on other side of glass. This is Boyle's first visit in two years since Welck has been in prison.

81

Young Boyle: I didn't have the guts to come here before. I don't know what I can do about this.

Young Welck (angry whisper): I do. (leans forward) You can start a savings account for me. Put half as much as you make every year out there into my account.

Young Boyle: Are you serious?

Young Welck: Hell yeah, I'm serious.

Young Boyle: I don't know if I can do that. Maybe when I'm doing better.

Young Welck: Better? I'd say you're doing a hell of a lot better than I am!

Young Boyle (fires back): I didn't ask you to do this. You were the one who said we both don't have to go down for this.

Young Welck (gets up, walks away): Go to hell, Jimmy.

Young Boyle: Larry! Larry!

{END OF BOYLE'S FLASHBACK}

Boyle turns off his shower water. He dreads meeting Welck tonight because he knows it's payback time or lose his business in a town that knows everyone's business.

*****

SERIES OF SHOTS:

That night, Kenny parks his Mustang near Mrs. Welck's car in front of her house and opens his trunk.

Bob pulls over the black prison van on the shoulder of the highway and parks. Welck, handcuffed in leg irons, watches Bob turn on his emergency flashers. Bob gets out of the van, slides open the side door and removes the cuffs and leg iron before tossing the bag of clothes at him.

Behind the football field bleachers, Kansas and Gary unload equipment from the Jeep and walk toward the street-lit football field.

In Boyle's house, Boyle is dressed after showering; he nervously checks his wrist watch.

In the moving Bingham van, inmate Welck rides on the front passenger seat wearing casual civilian clothes that includes a new pair of Nikes.

Parked in front of the high school, Kenny carries equipment from Mrs. Welck's parked car.

Under the bleachers, Kansas sets up her new equipment in this obscure spot under the visitors' bleachers as Gary inserts mic earbud.

Outside Mrs. Welck's house, Bob parks the prison van in front of her house. Larry Welck gets out of the van and into Kenny's Mustang, whereupon Welck drives Kenny's Mustang with Bob following.

At the high school football field on the fifty-yard-line at the middle of the field, Kenny sets up his camera on a tripod and tests a hidden mic.

Under the bleachers, Gary gives thumbs up sign to Kansas when he hears Kenny.

Target Jimmy Boyle exits his house, gets into his truck and drives away.

END SERIES OF SHOTS

*****

In front of the high school, Bob parks the prison van near Mrs. Welck's car and Kenny's Mustang, where Kenny and Welck wait on the sidewalk. Bob gets out of the van, slides the side door open, whereupon Kenny and Welck get inside the van along with Bob, who closes the door behind them. Bob is in a no-nonsense mood, unsure of what Boyle might do to his ex-quarterback.

Inside the van, Kenny hides a tiny mic under Welck's waistband as Bob gets in his prisoner's face.

    Bob (serious whisper): Larry. Look into my eyes. You mess this up and I'll make sure you never get out of Bingham. Stay with the script.

Welck is intimidated by Officer Fuller, nodding yes to Bingham's head security officer, who exits the van.

    Kenny (to Welck): No pressure, huh? (beat) Don't worry about me out there. Just go with the flow and walk with me to the middle of the field.

Outside the high school, Kenny and Welck exit the prison van and walk toward the football field as Bob drives the Bingham van to an obscure spot to observe Boyle's arrival and Mrs. Welck's car. Meanwhile:

Under the bleachers, Kansas can see with incredible clarity the black prison van with its tinted windows as well as Mrs. Welck's car and Kenny's Mustang. She sees Kenny and Welck walking toward the middle of the field. Gary and Kansas can HEAR the distant conversation via mic on Welck:

    Kansas (to Gary): This night-vision filter is incredible. I can see everything.

84

Gary (gripes): For three grand I would hope so.

Kansas (joking banter): Quit your complaining. We nail this scene and our lives change forever, Gary. Do you get that? I mean, this is Joe's ticket -

Gary: Yeah, I get it.

Kansas inserts an earpiece and we HEAR Kenny and Welck's conversation:

On the football field, Kenny and Welck reach the area where Kenny's camera is pointing at them, mounted on a tri-pod.

Kenny: I'll bet you never thought you'd be back here tonight.

Larry Welck: No way. Bob wouldn't tell me until we got to my mom's house.

Kenny picks up the football and they toss it back and forth.

Larry Welck (referring to camera): He won't want you filming this.

Kenny: Just play your role and I'll play mine.

*****

Meanwhile, Jimmy Boyle drives to the high school. He sees Kenny's Mustang parked in front of his old high school near Mrs. Welck's car. Boyle parks his truck in front of the school.

From the prison van's POV: Bob watches with night-vision binoculars as Boyle parks his truck.

Boyle gets out of his truck and walks toward the football field as:

Night-vision lens allows Kansas to see Boyle approaching.

Kansas (to Gary): Target approaching.

On the football field, Boyle sees Kenny hike the new football to Welck in shotgun formation as Kenny runs a slant pattern and Boyle completes a pass to Kenny. Boyle sees Kenny's camera and thinks this is being filmed. Welck spots his high school wide receiver and points for Boyle to spread wide left while Kenny gets ready to hike ball to quarterback Welck in shotgun position.

Larry Welck: Ninety-nine! Sixteen! Secret Fire! Secret Fire!!

Kenny hikes the ball to Welck and Kenny hustles to his camera to film Boyle diving for a long completion. Kenny has his camera pointed at these reunited teammates walking toward each other. Welck plays it friendly and cool by initiating a hug that Boyle wasn't expecting.

Larry Welck: Thanks for coming, Jimmy.

Jimmy Boyle: I can't believe you're out.

Larry Welck: It's like a dream.

Under the bleachers, Kansas and Gary can see and hear Welck and Boyle walk to the middle of the field. Boyle has the football and doesn't like Kenny filming them.

Jimmy Boyle (to Kenny): No way. No cameras. I'm not here to be interviewed.

Larry Welck (to Kenny): Yeah, maybe some other time.

Kenny picks up his camera equipment and walks away without the football.

Kenny: I'll call you tomorrow, Mr. Welck. (to Boyle) My ball, please!

Boyle gives Kenny his football, and Kenny heads for his car. Boyle and Welck stand a few feet apart.

Jimmy Boyle: What's this documentary about?

Larry Welck: It's about us.

Jimmy Boyle: Everything?

Larry Welck: Everything.

Jimmy Boyle: What can I do for you now to make this go away?

Larry Welck: Write me a check for a hundred and sixty grand.

Jimmy Boyle: Or what? You'll blackmail me?

Larry Welck: You can call it anything you want. I came here to tell you that Mr. Fleming will drop off his proposal to you tomorrow. This way I can help my mom and get something out of these last sixteen years.

Boyle watches Welck walk away toward his mother's car.

From behind the wheel of the prison van, Bob watches Welck drive away and soon follows his prisoner.

From under the bleachers, Kansas and Gary watch Boyle walk to his truck and drive away.

Kansas: That was good.

Gary: We'll find out how good tomorrow.

*****

SERIES OF SHOTS:

Outside Mrs. Welck's house, Bob waits behind the wheel of the Bingham van. Mrs. Welck's car is parked on the driveway as:

Inside Mrs. Welck's house, Larry Welck, in civilian clothes, holds his mother's hand while chatting at her kitchen table over coffee.

At Abilene RV park campsite, the crew is there. Lights are on in Traveller. Kansas edits tonight's meeting while Gary writes on the couch as:

In campsite shower, Kenny showers as:

Jimmy Boyle has returned home, and he looks depressed.

Bob has pulled the prison van off to the shoulder with flashers on as Welck changes back into his prison clothes.

Later, Bob returns the van to Bingham.

Bob escorts Welck back into his cell.

END SERIES OF SHOTS

*****

Later that night, Joe HEARS Bob's footsteps approaching from the dark cell block while lying on his bed. He hurries to his cell bars. They whisper:

Bob: I don't know what was said, but they were together on that field for at least five minutes.

Joe: Good. I told Welck to walk away after setting up Gary's proposal tomorrow. (changes subject) Tomorrow I got that interview with that Wichita kid, Boyd Jenkins, who killed his math teacher a few years ago.

Bob: Oh, yeah? What time's the interview?

Joe: Two. Text Kenny and tell him I want him to shoot the interview tomorrow with Jenkins.

Bob: The warden approved you shooting your interview?

Joe smiles while nodding yes.

Bob: Joseph Long, you've got some life in here. And I know you've got some interviews you could shoot in here that would sell big time outside these walls. People love to hear all the details from the bad guy himself.

Joe: You know as well as I do that most every guy in here was already bad long before they came here.

Bob: Uh-huh.

Joe: I don't want to exploit their crimes. Let the media do that.

Bob: I don't either, but these targets we send the crew on could get weird. I was sitting in that van tonight seeing all kinds of things that could go down.

Joe: I know. I was thinking how Boyle could kill Welck and just say Welck threatened him.

Bob: Then Boyle would be off the hook with us.

Joe: Well, not really. We'd have it all recorded. But Welck's dead and his mother sues The Corporation.

Bob: Bottom line, Joe, you've got something good in here that every prison needs. I'll bet you've stopped a hundred evil bastards from getting out of here.

Joe: I have to watch my back in here more than I ever did outside.

Bob: You've given Karen and Kenny good work too. And you'll get to see Kenny more if Warden Ted lets you shoot your interviews. I'm on to you, Joe Long.

Bob starts to walk away.

Joe: Text Kenny about the interview with Jenkins.

Bob (walks away): Will do.

*****

Later that night in Traveller, Gary's writing when he HEARS Joni Mitchell's song "Both Sides Now" coming from Shasta's open window. Gary stops to listen and knows some of the lyrics. He continues writing as the song plays through:

SERIES OF SHOTS:

NEXT DAY

In office supply business, Gary's dressed for business with his briefcase as he makes a copy of his proposal while Kansas makes a copy of the crew's documentary, *Secret Fire.*

Jimmy Boyle, seated behind his desk, sees confident G. K. Fleming enter his office carrying a briefcase. Gary sits across from Boyle, opens the briefcase and hands Boyle his proposal. Boyle reads the proposal with keen interest then hands Gary a cashier's check made out to G. K. Fleming for $160,000.00. Gary gives Boyle the original disc of the documentary and exits Boyle's office.

Outside Boyle's office, Gary has a smile on his face as he walks to the Jeep, whereupon Kansas drives them away.

Inside his bank, Gary deposits the cashier's check, then smiles upon leaving the bank after an easy target is completed.

Outside the bank, Gary gets into the Jeep, high-fives Kansas before she sends a text to:

In Bingham's Guard Central Station, Bob reads the text from Kansas and smiles.

Joe smiles after Bob signals Joe that the target paid with a thumbs up.

In Bingham dining hall, while seated at a table Welck gets good news from Bob.

In Mrs. Welck house, she refuses to take a check for nearly thirty-seven grand, as she explains to Gary why.

Outside Abilene homeless shelter, Kansas waits in her Jeep as:

In shelter director's office, Gary is there to see Mrs. Welck give grateful SHELTER DIRECTOR her share of thirty-seven grand after equipment expenses.

At Bingham's front entrance, Kenny carries his camera equipment toward entrance as the song fades out.

END SERIES OF SHOTS

*****

In Guard Central Station, Bob and Warden Ted watch and listen to Joe's interview.

In private visiting area room, Kenny's behind a mounted camera pointed at Joe interviewing inmate BOYD JENKINS, 18, angry Caucasian; they are seated at a table.

Joe (on camera): Boyd, tell me what happened that day in Mr. Peterson's geometry class.

Boyd Jenkins: I hate geometry ... and he embarrassed me.

Joe: Why did you hate him so much you could kill him?

91

Boyd Jenkins: He'd embarrass me by asking me for answers to formulas he'd write out on the blackboard. Hell, I never even understood the question.

The young killer's devious laugh gets to Kenny.

Joe: How did he embarrass you?

Boyd Jenkins: I just told you. By asking me stuff on purpose when he knew I didn't know the answer.

Joe: He's a teacher. Teachers aren't supposed to embarrass you.

Boyd Jenkins: That's right.

Joe: How did you kill Mr. Peterson?

Boyd Jenkins: I ran him over with my truck.

Joe: There isn't a drop of remorse in you for what you did. If this is how you feel in here ... you'll die in here an angry man.

Junck appears unmoved.

Joe: Boyd, there's someone I'd like you to meet. (directs Kenny) Camera off. (to surveillance camera) Bob, how long would it take to get Larry Welck in here?

Bob (on overhead speaker): Maybe twenty minutes.

Joe (appeals to Bob): Smoke break?

*****

A bit later, at Joe's private writing table, Kenny's now behind his camera as Joe interviews Jenkins with Larry Welck. Joe and Welck sit across the table from angry Boyd Jenkins with Bob standing nearby.

Joe (on camera to Jenkins): Larry was sent here when he was eighteen for killing a man with his car. He's been in here sixteen years. And in his case it was an accident. He could've been out eight years ago, however Larry chose to protect a friend and took the fall himself.

Boyd Jenkins (to Welck): Why would you do that?

Larry Welck: Because he was my best friend and I wanted to protect him.

Boyd Jenkins (scowls): No friend is worth one day in this place.

Bob and Joe exchange knowing looks.

Joe: Larry, is there anything you want to say to this young man?

Larry Welck (to Jenkins): I've seen plenty of men come in here angry. But I didn't. Anger came to me in here. I was angry at myself for what I let happen. You can't go back out there angry. Anger destroys. Find a way to lose your anger in here.

Kenny gets a good close-up of Jenkins taking in Welck's words.

Joe (directs Kenny): That's good!

Bob is on his pager. By the time Welck and Jenkins get up from the table, OFFICERS escort them away. Joe leans against the table as Kenny gathers equipment.

Joe (to Kenny): Have your sister edit this and send it to Bob.

Kenny: Dad, you did a good thing having Welck talk to that kid. I could tell he was really listening.

Joe: Did you hear the good news?

Kenny: What?

Joe: Boyle paid.

Kenny: Sweet.

Joe: Crew meeting Saturday. (beat) Maybe you can rent a house in Wichita.

Kenny: Kansas will find us something.

Bob: Kenny, we got to go.

Kenny hugs Joe and Joe watches Bob escort Kenny out of the prison.

*****

Outside, on the Bingham parking lot, Bob walks Kenny to his car.

Bob: Are you all going to rent a house together?

Kenny: Gary wants to try it. And Kansas wants more space.

Bob: I know that your dad spent twelve years creating this gig for you and your sister. There's State and private facilities interested in what Joe does here. (changes subject) Tell Kansas and Gary I want the three of you over for dinner at my crib before long.

Bob hands Kenny a note when they reach the Mustang.

Bob: Give that to Gary for me. Tell him to deliver my share anonymously. I don't want my name mentioned. Are we clear?

Kenny: Yes, sir.

They fist bump. Bob watches Kenny get into his Mustang and drive away while blaring rock music.

*****

Outside a rural house for lease, Kansas and Gary get out of the Jeep and walk up to a brick, single-story 1960-era ranch-style furnished home. We see a "Furnished House for Rent" sign in the front yard of large lot shaded by trees. They peer into open windows.

Kansas: Fireplace, wood floors, the furniture looks -

Gary: Rustic?

Kansas: Yeah. I like it.

Gary: It's an old country house with lots of parking. Lots of space between neighbors. I like it. How long is the lease?

Kansas: Six months. It's twelve hundred a month plus utilities.

Gary: Call the number and see if we can look inside. And have Kenny come look at it.

Kansas (dials number): Kenny doesn't need to look at it. If I like it, he'll like it.

*****

Meanwhile, Joe enters affable Warden Ted's office. The warden is seated behind his cluttered desk; he's looking for a letter in his desk drawers.

Warden Ted: Please have a seat, Joe.

The warden finds the letter, gives it to Joe, which he reads while seated across from the warden's desk. Joe hands the letter back to the warden.

Warden Ted: What do you think?

Joe: I think it's terrific. When do I go?

Warden Ted: Soon.

95

Joe: I'll only go if my escort is Bob Fuller.

Warden Ted: I already asked Bob. (smiles) He's happy to take you.

Joe smiles.

Warden Ted: How lucky is it for you that one of my best correctional officers is your foster brother?

Joe: I know.

Warden Ted: I remember the day he applied for a position here. He was sitting in that very chair when he told me he had to start right away and he had to move up fast like he did at the Wichita Boys Club. If I remember right, it wasn't long after you arrived here that I hired Bob.

Joe smiles at Warden Ted's affable, knowing gaze.

Warden Ted: And I always thought it strange that Bob took a considerable cut in pay when he started here.

Joe: I know he's made my time here easier. I don't have a better friend, I know that.

Warden Ted nods in agreement.

Warden Ted (changes subject): Your request for Lawrence Welck's parole hearing was approved and added to this month's hearings.

Joe: That's great news. When is it?

Warden Ted: A week from today. (beat) And David Slovik is up for parole at the same hearing.

That's not good news to Joe.

In Bingham dining hall alone, Joe sits with a cup of coffee while writing at a back table:

Joe (voice over writing)*: Today has to be one of the best days I've had in here. This second easy one will keep my kids happy and ready for more good work. Part of this good day came when my warden approved my trip to Nebraska with Bob. Warden Ellen in this women's minimum-security prison wants me to train three of her inmates to do what I do in here. In twelve years I've helped solve at least a dozen cold missing persons' cases. I know of at least forty inmates who deserve a parole hearing to review incredible mitigating circumstances. None of these men are innocent, yet deserve consideration, like Larry Welck. What really concerns me are the cold-blooded men in here who will get out of here one day because of time served. They will harm people again. That's the ugly truth about our penal system. There's one man in here I'm particularly concerned about. His name is David Slovik.*

Outside, at Bingham's inmate workout area, we see mean-looking, muscular Caucasian inmate DAVID SLOVIK, 40-45, lifting weights, going through a routine as:

Joe (voice over): *Slovik is up for a parole hearing the same day as Larry Welck. Slovik is a mean bastard who has spent seven years in here for sexually assaulting old ladies in hospitals. I've interviewed Slovik and there's no way I'd release this man out into the world again. I understand that two of his three victims who testified against him are now deceased, so that improves his chances that nobody will testify against him at his parole hearing.*

Back to Bingham dining hall, Joe stops writing and takes wincing sip of cold coffee.

Joe (voice over): *I've got to try something.*

SERIES OF SHOTS:

Kenny walks through the same furnished house with Kansas, who finds that the cupboards are furnished like a vacation home. The ELDERLY LANDLORD is going over the lease agreement with Gary at the large dining table near the kitchen.

That night in Traveller, Gary gives happy Kenny and Kansas their checks. That's when Kenny gives Gary the note Bob gave him earlier today. Gary reads Bob's note.

Outside the Wichita Boys Club, Kenny waits in his parked Mustang as Gary hands grateful BOYS CLUB DIRECTOR a check.

Outside Crew's new rental house, all vehicles are parked in front of the same rental house as Kenny, Kansas, and Gary move their things into the house. Shasta is parked and not attached to Traveller.

In Bingham's family visiting area, the crew sits at a table with Joe as Joe shows them inmate mug shot of David Slovik from his file.

In crew's house, Kansas is on her phone talking to someone from Slovik's file as Gary and Kenny listen.

Next day, Kansas is behind a camera as Gary interviews elderly MARIE HOLLAND, 80-85, Caucasian, as HOLLAND'S FAMILY sits with her in their family home.

That night in crew's house, Kansas cooks a meal in her new kitchen and serves Gary and Kenny, who are seated at their dining table. The crew toasts to their new home.

END SERIES OF SHOTS

*****

At a prisoner review board hearing in Wichita, three seated middle-aged PAROLE BOARD OFFICERS, one woman and two men, are ready to announce their decision to standing and handcuffed Larry Welck. Bob stands behind his prisoner.

Parole Board Officer (reading from paper): Upon review of Lawrence Welck's case, this board has decided to grant parole and release Mr. Welck from the Bingham Facility as soon as possible.

Larry Welck is stunned to tears of joy and Bob is happy for Welck. Bob escorts Welck out of the room and returns with handcuffed inmate David Slovik, who stands at table facing parole board. Bob opens Joe's laptop on the table and puts the screen in front of inmate Slovik.

Parole Board Officer: Mr. Slovic, we'd like you to watch the screen in front of you.

Bob plays Gary's interview with Marie Holland, one of Slovik's victims.

Gary (off screen): Marie Holland, why do this interview?

Marie Holland (on laptop screen): I'm one of the three women Mr. Slovik assaulted. The other two are dead. I have to speak for them too when I say that man should never be free to hurt anyone again. That's all I have to say.

Bob closes the laptop. Slovik's eyes are averted down like the slime ball he is.

Parole Board Officer: Mr. David Slovik … your parole is denied.

Smiling Bob escorts dejected Slovic out of the room. Soon Bob returns to pick up Joe's laptop from the table.

*****

NEXT DAY

Inside a moving Bingham van, Joe rides on the front passenger seat wearing civilian clothes, as Bob, also in civilian clothes, drives the black unmarked van with tinted windows past a Nebraska state line marker on Highway 77 North.

Bob: So here we are, on our way to this women's prison where you'll train three inmates to do what you do.

Joe: Surreal huh? (beat) The warden has a bunch of applicants and she wants me to pick three.

Bob: Amazing. (changes subject) I got a text from Kansas inviting me to dinner when we get back. They want me to see their new crib.

Joe: Did Gary give you your share?

Bob nods yes and he knows what's coming.

Joe: You gave your share to the Boys Club.

Bob (smiles big): Yep. And Mrs. Welck gave her share to the homeless shelter in Abilene.

Joe: You know this is good work we're doing. (beat) Can we stop in Beatrice to eat at this place I know?

*****

Bob and Joe are eating at a booth in a Beatrice, Nebraska cafe.

Bob: Tell me, how many men go to prison to find their calling? The best thing you did this week was keep that Slovik creep locked up.

Joe: There's too many like him that get released and still hate the world. (changes subject) Bobby, after we eat, there's something I'd like to do.

100

*****

Later, the prison van radio blasts "Amie" by Pure Prairie League as Joe now drives the van and sings while Bob rides shotgun and mimics playing guitar. The song fades out as the van drives north on a rural Nebraska highway.

*****

Meanwhile, outside Bingham's front entrance, Larry Welck is leaving prison a free man in the same clothes he wore recently in Abilene. Larry walks toward his mother's parked car, where his mother stands outside the front passenger door smiling at him. They embrace. Then Jimmy Boyle gets out from behind the wheel of his mother's car and leans on the roof of the car smiling. Larry is wary and confused.

Mrs. Welck: Jimmy was doing some jobs around my house when you called for me to pick you up.

Old friends smile at each other. After Larry helps his mother onto the back seat:

Jimmy Boyle: Larry, you ride in back with your mom. (smiles) This time...I'll drive.

Larry smiles while riding on the back seat with his happy mother. Boyle drives them away as "Amie" by Pure Prairie League plays.

End of Episode 2

101

Episode 3:

The Big Squeeze

L ate afternoon, Bob parks the black Bingham van a ways back from a Nebraska corrections facility for women. Bob and Joe wear civilian clothes. Joe sits on the front passenger seat. Both men look at The Corporation's minimum/maximum security facility for women.

Joe: What do you know about this place?

Bob: It's our only women's facility in Nebraska. The warden is pro-active for rehabilitation with an average recidivism rate.

Joe (looking at prison): Since when is average good? (beat) How many inmates?

Bob: About three hundred.

Joe: The best stories in there ... only a woman could get.

Bob (Bob's humor): That's why you're here.

Joe chuckles at his friend's humor.

Bob: We'll see about those stories tomorrow. Let's get a room.

Joe (grins): I thought you'd never ask.

Bob laughs with Joe as they drive away from the facility.

Later, at a rural Nebraska motel, the unmarked black Bingham van is parked outside a room of a privately-owned 12-unit motel. An abandoned farmhouse is located near the motel on a hill.

In Joe and Bob's motel room, Joe and Bob watch the MUTED TV screen while stretched out on queen-size beds.

Joe (enjoying moment): I may not move from here till morning.

Bob laughs while rubbing his sore back.

    Joe: Can we order a pizza?

    Bob: Yeah, if it's thin crust.

Excited Joe finds a phone book and hands it to Bob.

    Joe: I'll get some ice.

While Bob orders a pizza, Joe grabs the ice bucket and leans close to the mirror to see his image in real glass for the first time in 12 years. He touches his gray hair.

At dusk, in Joe and Bob's motel room, Bob and Joe eat pizza in bed.

    Bob: You know why the warden is paying me to escort you here?

    Joe: So I don't run off.

    Bob: Yes ... and he wants you to replicate what you do in Bingham in other facilities. So tomorrow might be the biggest day of Joe Long's life.

    Joe (nods in agreement): I know that.

*****

NEXT DAY

Joe, in his Bingham royal blue jumpsuit, is escorted by uniformed Bob into the women's correctional facility after WOMEN OFFICERS process them.

In the prison waiting area, Bob and Joe sit together waiting to see Warden Ellen.

Receptionist: Mr. Fuller and Mr. Long, Warden Ellen can see you now.

Bob and Joe enter the warden's office. WARDEN ELLEN, 55-60, corpulent and jolly Caucasian, greets her guests with a standing handshake and invites them to sit down. She is most anxious to get Joe's system working in her prison.

Warden Ellen: How was your trip?

Both visitors answer at once:

Bob & Joe: Fine, thanks.

They all chuckle.

Warden Ellen: Mr. Long, I first heard about your interviews from an inmate here who has a brother incarcerated at Bingham. She had good things to say, and I simply had to call your warden inquiring about you. I hope you can train three of our inmates to interview our prison population, all in the name of rehabilitation.

Joe (frankly): I'm a wannabe journalist at heart, Warden Ellen. I have no professional credentials whatsoever. I'm a high school graduate with an ear and eye for legitimate discontent and sociopathic tendencies. I ask the right questions.

104

Joe hands Warden Ellen a piece of paper from his file folder that she reads quickly.

Warden Ellen (after reading): Interesting.

Joe: Warden, I understand you have several prospects in mind, and you want me to train three of your inmates?

Warden Ellen: That's right.

Joe: I want to interview all the prospective interviewers together.

Warden Ellen (curious): How would that work?

*****

Later that day, on the facility softball field, Joe paces in front of 10 FEMALE INMATES of all ages and ethnicities; they are wearing orange jumpsuits and seated on bleachers along with Warden Ellen and Bob, who sit by themselves on the back row of the same stand of bleachers. Joe lights a cigarette.

Joe: The warden says I can pick three of you to interview your prison population. (beat) I must say, ladies that my twelve years of incarceration have flown by because of these interviews I lucked into. (smoking) My mother always told me to find a way to serve people. Well, here I am, in prison, and serving more people than I ever did outside. (beat) The fact remains that I have to pick three of you to train. On a scale of one to ten, ten being the ultimate, show me with both hands those of you that rate this opportunity as something more important than anything else to you right now.

Three FEMALE INMATE TRAINEES raise both hands and Joe points to each one.

Joe: You three are in. Follow me.

Joe walks away as the three grateful chosen inmate trainees get up from the bleachers and follow Joe. The warden and Bob are confused yet impressed amidst the grumbling seven inmates who weren't chosen.

Joe walks the prison yard with the three inmate trainees.

Joe: First off, I want to know why each of you were sent here. I'll start with myself. (beat) Twelve years ago I plea-bargained for twenty years without parole for the second-degree murder of my wife with mitigating circumstances.

Joe points to inmate trainee #1 to go next.

Inmate Trainee #1: Embezzlement. Twelve years.

Inmate Trainee #2: Arson. Three years.

Inmate Trainee #3: Grand theft. Ten years.

Joe: An interesting story is there in each of you. The first question I'd ask any of you is how you got here. After I really listen to your story, I'd ask you if you deserve to be here. The ones who say no are the interesting stories with mitigating circumstances. Those are the files I keep working on. The ones that answer yes, that they deserve to be here, will gladly give you all the awful details of their crimes. There's no healing for those inmates. The numbers in Bingham Prison are nine yes for every no. The most important information you can gather is finding the inmates who have no business getting out. That's life-saving work and you must do it. Everybody get that?

The trainees all respond that they get it while they continue walking.

Joe: The questions I give you on a script will keep you organized and on track during your interviews. There will be interesting information gathered that must be given to your warden

ASAP. Follow the script, listen, and make accurate notations on each file.

Joe stops walking. The trainees stop to listen to him.

Joe: Where can we get a cup of coffee around here?

*****

A bit later, in the empty prison dining hall, Joe, Bob, and Warden Ellen sit on one side of a table having coffee with the same 3 trainee inmates seated across from them. Each trainee has a copy of Joe's interview script.

Joe (to inmates): All you really have to do is follow that script and listen. Everyone has a story. You'll hear and know the things you should write down.

Joe connects into the eyes of each trainee.

Joe: My warden is pleased that his recidivism rate is the lowest it's ever been in Bingham. I want you to document everything important in your notebooks right away, or you'll lose it. You'll have several sessions with some inmates. You're really at the heart and guts of what's wrong with our society. These are the people we learn from and sure as hell want living a good life when they join the outside world that just locked them up for an average of four years and three months. The most important thing you'll do is mark the bottom line of every file of every inmate, deciding whether that inmate is a danger to society when she gets out of here.

Bob (tension breaker): But no pressure, ladies!

They all laugh.

*****

That early evening, Bob and Joe, both in civilian clothes, are having dinner in quiet rural cafe booth when Bob speed-dials a number on

107

his cell phone and places his phone on the table with the speaker phone on. Kansas is (off screen) when on her phone.

Kansas (on speaker phone): Hey!

Bob (playful): Is this Karen?

Kansas (on speaker phone): Hi, Bob.

Bob: Hey, Kansas. You're on speaker phone. Your dad and I are having dinner in this quiet café not far from Lincoln, Nebraska.

Kansas: Really?

Joe (leans to cell phone): Hey, Kansas! How's the new crib?

Kansas: I really like it. It's the biggest and nicest place we've ever lived in. What's up in Nebraska?

Joe: I'm enjoying a meal with Bob! (looks out window) In Nebraska!

Kansas: I'm happy for you!

Joe: Tell the guys to lay low a couple weeks. After that easy one, I want to finish up here in a few days and get back to my files and find another easy one. How's that sound?

Kansas: Sounds good to me.

Joe: What's Kenny up to?

Kansas: He's with Gary shopping for a flat screen TV.

Joe: So Gary's living there?

Kansas: He says he wants to go month-to-month with it. Gary had to pay Kenny's first month's rent.

Joe: Why's that?

Kansas: Gary told Kenny that if he used Kenny's idea to have Boyle and Welck meet at their old football field, he'd pay Kenny's first month's rent.

Bob and Joe laugh.

Bob (to cell phone): We'll text you.

Joe: Bye, love you.

Kansas: Love you, too. Bye.

Bob picks up his cell phone from table and puts it in his shirt pocket.

Joe: I'll need more than a few days to train three inmates. It takes time to make sure it's done right.

Bob: Who do you think you're talking to?

Joe: What?

Bob: You want the crew up here … to spend time with Kenny and Karen.

Joe: That's right. (beat) And I also heard from all three trainees that an inmate here by the name of Mary Lake Day has an interesting story.

Bob: What's her story?

Joe: That's what you're going to find out tomorrow. Even the warden said I should interview this Mary Lake Day. See if there's something there.

*****

NEXT DAY

Inside the all-women guard break room, uniformed Bob laughs and chats with 5 uniformed FEMALE GUARDS of mixed races and ages 30-50.

Bob: A man can't interview a woman and get the real good stuff. Anyway, you're the guards who know the good stories. Tell me about Mary Lake Day.

The guards laugh and agree that Mary Lake Day is a good story. African-American, GUARD BARBARA, 40s, does the talking for all the guards.

Guard Barbara (to Bob): Mary and her sister, Larayne, had a bookmobile. And she was delivering more than books to her patrons. Mary had a greenhouse in her Omaha back yard.

Bob: Weed?

Guard Barbara: This was a hybrid weed Mary and Larayne grew exclusively to get Larayne off morphine. Larayne was a librarian at a grade school in Omaha before her accident that left her paralyzed from the waist down. The bookmobile and greenhouse were in Mary's name.

Bob: So Mary took the fall.

Guard Barbara: She had a few hundred bookmobile customers, mostly her so-called "Disabled Vets," who bought her home grown marijuana for pain management. And she proved at her trial she used all the proceeds from sales to pay for the bookmobile service that saved the County hundreds of thousands of dollars.

Bob: How can I talk to this Mary Lake Day?

Guard Barbara (looks at watch): She won't talk to reporters or writers. But she'll talk to you.

The other guards laugh.

Bob: Why's that?

*****

Later, in the otherwise empty prison dining hall, Bob sits alone at a table with coffee until Guard Barbara escorts MARY LAKE DAY to his table. Mary is a middle-aged African American, attractive and flirtatious, and attracted to Bob.

Guard Barbara (curt introduction): Officer Bob. Mary Lake Day. Take a seat.

Guard Barbara gives them privacy, leaving the dining hall.

Bob: Would you like some coffee?

Mary Lake Day (smiles): No thanks.

Bob: When do you get out of here?

Mary Lake Day: Practically never.

Bob laughs at her sense of humor.

Mary Lake Day: I'm up for parole in about six months.

Bob: And you've been in here how long?

Mary Lake Day: Three years and a couple months. They got me for growing weed and distributing. Most of the people on my route had medical marijuana prescriptions. And some of my disabled vets only bought their weed from me to support the bookmobile service. They're good people.

Bob: I definitely feel that's one creative way to serve a bunch of folks in need.

Mary Lake Day (leans forward): Frankly, Bob, if I got out of here tomorrow, I'd move to Colorado and get another route going. People love to read when they feel high.

Bob laughs as:

*****

In a private facility room, Inmate Trainee #1 interviews INMATE BRENDA, an elderly Caucasian; they are being watched by a surveillance camera:

In Warden Ellen's office, Joe and the warden watch and listen to the interview on a laptop screen:

Inmate Trainee #1 (on monitor with script): Why did you agree to do this interview?

Inmate Brenda (on monitor): I heard about that Kansas guy, Joe Long, who does these interviews. I think it's a cool thing.

Inmate Trainee #1 (on monitor): Of all the inmates here, why would you be one of the first interviewed?

Inmate Brenda (on monitor): I guess 'cause I've been here the longest.

The trainee checks her script:

Inmate Trainee #1: Why are you here?

Inmate Brenda: I killed my husband before he could kill me.

Inmate Trainee #1: So you were defending yourself?

Inmate Brenda: Not really. He was asleep.

Joe takes notes.

*****

112

Meanwhile, back in the prison dining hall, Bob and Mary Lake Day are still talking at a table in the empty dining hall.

Mary Lake Day: I started my little bookmobile service delivering a little weed to our Disabled Vets. Trouble was, I'd have this customer buying weed for his granny with glaucoma, and that customer for his uncle with gout. Before long I was dealing more weed than books.

Bob: Take me through a memorable day for Mary Lake Day back then.

Mary Lake Day: That's easy. It was after my arraignment when all my Disabled Vets were there and they helped me make bail. (changes subject) Half the women in here are sisters from Omaha who heard of us.

Bob: I think your sister's story would interest Mr. Fleming.

Mary Lake Day: He's the guy who makes the documentaries.

Bob: Right.

*****

Later, Joe, now in civilian clothes, is enjoying his lunch in a cafe booth with uniformed Bob.

Bob: I talked to Mary Lake Day.

Joe: Is there a target?

Bob: I don't know.

Joe: I know three people who could find out. And we will need more time here.

Bob nods in agreement before calling Warden Ted on his cell phone.

*****

Meanwhile, in the crew's rental house, Kansas and Gary are having a healthy lunch at the dining room table when late-riser Kenny comes out of his room wearing only boxer shorts. His body is thin and he's not in shape.

Kansas: Get a shirt on.

Kenny turns around and heads back to his room.

Gary (to Kansas): Thank you. (beat) Was he out all night?

Kansas: I don't care. I'm not his guardian now that he's eighteen and out of high school.

Gary (discreetly): Should we talk to him?

Kansas: It wouldn't do any good. His problem is he's not busy enough. The last job was too easy.

Kenny comes out wearing a T-shirt over his boxers. He goes into the kitchen to get his breakfast cereal to eat at the table.

Gary (discreetly to Kansas): You're right. He has too much free time. When I was his age I was scared shitless about going to 'Nam while pumping gas for two bucks an hour.

Kenny eats his cereal at the table as Kansas gets a new text message from Bob.

Kansas (reads text): Warden Ted granted extension. Joe wants crew to come up to Nebraska ASAP for prospect that may not have target. Possible good work here.

Kansas and Gary look at each other as Kenny eats.

Gary (to Kansas): Nebraska? May not have a target?

114

Kenny: We're going to Nebraska?

Kansas (looking at Gary). Looks like it.

Kenny: Sweet.

Gary (to Kenny): What's so sweet about going to Nebraska?

Kenny (shrugs): I've never been there.

Gary rolls his eyes; he's upset with a text that has no target potential.

Gary (to both): I thought we were waiting for our next case.

Kansas gets up to clear the dishes from the table.

Kansas (to Gary): This is our next case. (to Gary & Kenny) You better hook up Shasta to Traveller.

Gary: Why don't you get a trailer hitch for your Jeep?

Kansas (clears dishes): I thought we'd use the Jeep to run errands like we did on the last case.

Gary gets up and clears his dirty dishes as Kenny shovels in his cereal.

Gary (resigned): Your dad wants us in Nebraska ... we go to Nebraska.

Kenny (to annoy Gary): Sweet.

Gary: Yeah. Sweet.

*****

That early evening, in Bob and Joe's motel room, Bob exits the bathroom after showering; he's wearing only his boxers. The TV is on and Joe is gone. Bob opens the motel room door and doesn't see his prisoner outside.

*****

A bit later, at a nearby abandoned farmhouse overlooking the motel from a hilltop, Joe sits on the rickety-old porch steps of the abandoned farmhouse. He smokes a cigarette looking at the view with two cans of soda iced beside him in the motel room's ice bucket. His eyes enjoy every moment of this freedom. Before long, Bob appears on foot in casual clothes. Bob sits down next to his friend. Bob opens a can of iced soda and takes a long drink.

Joe (enjoying view): How'd you know to find me here?

Bob: How many times did we pool our money to get a bottle of pop and hang out in old places like this?

Joe smiles in agreement while focusing on the view.

Joe: I want to get a place in the country when I get out. (to horizon) Until the first year or so I imagined myself getting out and being more social … traveling, meeting new people. Then, as the years passed in there I wanted a quiet place, somewhere to get away from that "Big Squeeze."

Bob laughs.

Bob: Big Squeeze. I haven't heard that since we were in school.

Joe: That's what we called every foster parent, cop and teacher.

Bob & Joe (together): Big Squeeze.

They laugh.

Bob: Brother, you are in the ultimate … no, penultimate Big Squeeze.

116

Joe: You think I don't know that? If I make it out of there alive in eight years, I'll feel like I can handle anything out here. (refers to cigarette) Hell, I might even quit smoking. (beat) You smoked. How'd you quit?

Bob: When I got that Boys Club gig, I decided to give 'em up. I thought a Boys Club director who smokes is a bit of a hypocrite when it comes to enforcing bans for smoking. We had a strict no-smoking rule on premises for employees and zero tolerance for boys caught smoking on the grounds. (laughs) Every morning, Joe, before opening our doors I'd see twenty boys smoking across the street. They looked like penguins huddled together in the winter.

Joe: Yeah, and how many times did we steal cigarettes?

Bob: You, Joseph Long, stole a carton of Larks. Man, those were awful. And we smoked those nasty things for two, three months.

Bob laughs with his foster brother.

Bob (changes subject): I got a text from Karen on the way up here. They'll be here tonight. She said she'd text me for directions to the motel when she gets closer to Lincoln.

Joe grabs a soda from the ice bucket, walks along the old farmhouse porch and opens the can while thinking about something.

Bob: What is it?

Joe: I was just feeling strange about meeting my kids here.

Bob: You do know Kenny smokes weed?

Joe: Yeah, I smell it on his clothes every time I see him.

Joe looks out to the horizon, taking in this moment of freedom.

*****

117

Later, when Bob and Joe walk back to their motel room they see that the motel's parking lot is full, mostly with passenger vans.

*****

That night, lying on beds watching TV, Bob gets a text message and reads it.

Bob: They're twenty minutes away. I'll call Karen and tell her how to get here.

Joe: You better not call her Karen.

Joe gets up, gets the ice bucket and leaves their room while Bob calls Kansas on his cell phone.

Joe carries the ice bucket to the ice machine where a middle-aged African American woman in a wheelchair gets ice for herself. They exchange smiles and she rolls away with her ice. Joe fills his ice bucket and walks over to an obscure place on the parking lot to have a cigarette. Joe sees other DISABLED VETS coming and going, getting settled into rooms. Joe wants to find out who these people are and walks toward the motel registration lobby.

*****

Later that night, the crew's vehicles are parked on the motel's lot. Inside Bob and Joe's motel room, Bob and Gary sit on chairs as Kenny and Kansas relax on the beds while they all listen to Joe as he paces the motel room.

Joe: Just before you guys arrived, the motel manager told me it's some kind of Mary Lake Day support gathering on the facility parking lot tomorrow.

Gary (to Bob & Joe): So you met with this Mary Lake Day and there doesn't seem to be a target?

Joe: Sometimes Gary, there's a good cause and no target. And, there's a disturbing number of men and women incarcerated for recreation and small-time drug use or distribution. Mary Lake Day represents that. (to crew) This thing we do is not always about an easy target. I think when we run across a story - like Mary Lake Day - we should pursue it and see where it goes.

Kansas (to Joe): So we'll interview this Mary Lake Day and other inmates who know Mary while we're here?

Joe: So far, that's what we have.

Kenny: Then what?

Joe: It's too early to know. Tomorrow I want you and your sister behind a camera. (to Kenny) You have to be the front man and get those release forms signed. (to crew) I do want to say that I know we could dig and find more interesting stories or bizarre crimes, but this Mary Lake Day thing was set up because I was coming here. (to Gary) Yeah, I'd like to see where this goes.

Kansas: What if we gave half of any money we take in from this project to Mary's Disabled Vets?

Gary: After expenses.

Bob: That's a great idea … Kansas.

Kansas smiles at Bob.

Kansas: Are we staying here tonight?

Joe: They're full up.

Bob: The motel manager told me we got the last room.

Gary: We could stay parked here. I'm sure the motel won't mind.

Bob: You could all grab a shower in here tomorrow morning.

Kenny (stands): I'm going for a walk.

Gary and Kansas know what that means. After Kenny leaves the motel room:

Joe (to Bob): It is a nice night for a walk.

Bob nods yes and Joe exits the motel room.

*****

Soon, Joe catches up with Kenny right when his son is taking a hit from his pipe. It's awkward for Kenny as they walk together up the hill toward the same ancient farmhouse, its dark silhouette lit in the moonlight at the top of the hill. As they walk:

Joe: That's what this Mary Lake Day thing is about.

Kenny: Weed?

Joe: Medical marijuana. Should it be legalized in Nebraska? There's a bunch of people here tonight who think so.

Kenny: It's not legal anywhere for me.

Joe (smiles): Doesn't stop you, does it?

Kenny laughs.

Joe (curious): When did you start smoking weed?

Kenny: The summer after my junior year.

Joe: When you started working at that chicken joint.

Kenny: Yeah. This guy there would rave about his weed he bought in Colorado. I was the last one to try it. We'd get high after work.

Joe: Uh-huh. (beat) Karen must've known.

Kenny: Yeah. She said I could only smoke it in her trailer, alone, and I had to keep my grades up.

Joe: That's not a bad deal.

Kenny: Yeah. I got to buy my own weed.

Joe: Instead of sneaking around.

Kenny: Yeah. Gary says we can't smoke during a job. But we can after hours.

Joe: Gary smokes, too?

Kenny: Oh, yeah. His weed's better than mine. He's pretty stingy with it. He says it stimulates curiosity and changes his thought patterns.

Joe: Mary Lake Day told Bob that she and her sister grew this hybrid pot plant that enabled her sister to get off morphine cold turkey. I really don't know the science behind it all, but her customers on her bookmobile route thought enough of Mary to help her make bail. She said that she and her sister Larayne grew this hybrid of pot that shrinks tumors and eases chronic pain with insulin benefits.

Kenny: That says a lot for her work.

Joe leads the way to the abandoned farmhouse up ahead.

Joe: Bob and I were up here earlier. I'd live here now if I could.

Joe and Kenny sit on the front porch steps of the abandoned farmhouse. Joe lights a cigarette and looks out into the quiet darkness of rural Nebraska.

Joe: Earlier I was up here alone and I used my imagination to try and see how the people might've lived here. To do that is real joy.

Kenny: That's why I like my music. It stimulates my -

Joe: Curiosity?

They laugh.

Kenny: This is all so strange sitting here now with you. Warden Ted must really like you, to let you come here, Dad.

Joe: Yeah. He hadn't been at Bingham long when I first got there. I came up with this interview thing as a way to get out of my own head. The warden liked the data I was giving him. (beat) Plus he really likes Bob.

They laugh.

Joe: I read somewhere that every man must cure himself of that feeling of life-emptiness. I found my cure these last twelve years.

Kenny: I know you have, Dad.

Joe: All we have is now, and tomorrow if we're lucky. And I have a feeling you'll be one busy front man tomorrow.

*****

NEXT DAY

Kenny parks his Mustang on the Nebraska women's facility parking lot; he's amazed at the fleet of handicapped-equipped vans parked on the lot. He sees dozens of DISABLED VETS of all ages in wheelchairs parked along the front prison entrance sidewalk. A man in a wheelchair holds up a sign that reads: "FREE MARY LAKE DAY". Kenny gets his camera equipment and a stack of release forms from his trunk and walks toward this impressive gathering of disabled vets in wheelchairs. Near the prison's main entrance, Kenny, coached by Joe, plays the role of front man, adroitly shooting his camera as he approaches a group of parked disabled vets. Kenny addresses them while handing out release forms.

Kenny (to group): I represent G. K. Fleming's film crew! The crew will be here soon to interview you about Mary Lake Day! If you want to be in the documentary, sign and date the form and give it back to me! Mr. Fleming will not interview you if you do not sign the release form!

Disabled Vet (to Kenny): What if we don't want to be interviewed or sign anything?

Kenny (handing out forms): Then you'll just be a blur on the screen or edited out!

Most of the disabled vets are anxious and receptive to signing the form.

Disabled Vet (off screen): Here comes the warden!

Warden Ellen arrives at work and walks by this peaceful gathering as Kenny films her approach.

Kenny (off screen): Warden, what can you say about this support for Mary Lake Day?

Warden Ellen (on camera): Are you with Mr. Fleming's crew?

Kenny (off screen): Yes.

The warden stops to talk to Kenny.

Warden Ellen (on camera): I can tell you Mary Lake Day has six months to serve for growing and distributing marijuana in Nebraska.

Two women officers exit the facility and approach their boss. When the warden tries to walk to the front entrance of her prison, disabled vets in wheelchairs block her way The warden stops her officers from taking action.

Warden Ellen (to group on camera): What do you want from me?

Kenny (off screen to warden): I'll tell you what these people want! You got an inmate out of prison in Kansas to interview Mary Lake Day! These people want you to bring Mary Lake Day to them, so they can be a part of it!

CHEERS from Mary's supporters. The warden appears to be considering something when she sees from her point of view:

On the parking lot, the film crew has arrived, unloading equipment from vehicles as Bob, in uniform, escorts Joe in inmate jumpsuit toward the gathering.

Joe (walking with Bob): Tell Gary I'll do this interview. Tell Kenny and Kansas to keep me off-camera.

Gary can see that Joe is directing this interview and wants to learn from Joe. The Disabled Vets circle around Joe, Bob, and Warden Ellen as Bob whispers Joe's orders to Kenny and then Kansas as Kansas gets behind her camera.

Joe: Warden, I'm sure you know Mary Lake Day's story better than I do. Why are all these people here today?

Warden Ellen (on camera): Mary had a sister named Larayne. She was a grade school librarian when she had a terrible fall and became paraplegic. Larayne had big problems with morphine addiction. Mary developed and grew this CBD-rich marijuana into a pain-killing plant that managed Larayne's reduced need for morphine. And I believe these people know this to be true.

124

APPLAUSE from the gathering.

Joe (off screen): How did the bookmobile play a role in the lives of these people?

Warden Ellen: That's something Mary should tell you.

Joe (off screen): Can I talk to Mary?

Warden Ellen: Follow me.

As Bob escorts Joe toward the front entrance, Gary checks the signed release forms with Kenny and Kansas.

Disabled Vets (chant off screen): WE WANT MARY! WE WANT MARY!

*****

Mary is happy to see her warden and Bob enter her cell with Joe. They introduce Joe to Mary. Joe looks around her cell until:

Joe: Warden, may I suggest something?

*****

A bit later, outside on the facility parking lot, Joe and Mary Lake Day are seated at a table with Kenny and Kansas filming the interview with her Disabled Vets. Bob stands nearby with correctional officers. Gary and Warden Ellen stand behind the disabled vets parked in wheelchairs, all listening to the interview.

Joe (off screen): Mary Lake Day, you're not only the first woman I've interviewed, you're the first good story I've come across. (works crowd) And I know your Disabled Vets, as you call them, are happy to be here with you, thanks to Warden Ellen!

APPLAUSE for Mary and the warden, which the warden appreciates.

125

Joe: I understand your sister Larayne inspired you to start your own bookmobile service?

Mary Lake Day (fondly on camera): Larayne loved books. And after her fall left her completely paralyzed from the waist down, I know that leaving her job as children's librarian only exacerbated her pain. My sister got hooked on morphine. We started growing our own plants to find the perfect pain-killer.

Joe: Didn't you say she was able to get totally off the morphine?

Mary Lake Day: That's right.

Joe: How did your neighbors not see the plants in your greenhouse?

Mary Lake Day (laughs): We grew corn along the windows. People couldn't see inside or just walk up to it. One of our patrons installed a security fence for us.

Joe: Can you tell us a little bit about your operation?

Mary Lake Day: We'd have certain times on certain days we'd park on a street and they'd come by, pick up their books they'd ordered last time, and we'd have their medication ready inside the book.

Joe (curious): How would they pay for it?

Mary Lake Day: They'd put their money in a little envelope we gave them to put inside the book when they returned it. We'd check the envelope and put the product back into the envelope inside their new books, and off they'd go.

Joe: Boy, I wish our library did that.

The audience laughs.

Joe: Then you got busted.

Mary Lake Day: Yes, sir.

Joe: What about Larayne?

Mary Lake Day: The house and bookmobile were in my name. Larayne was just one of my customers. That's the way it had to be.

Understanding nod from Joe.

Joe: Is your sister still in Omaha?

Mary Lake Day: She died in a nursing home six weeks after she got there. I know it was the meds they gave her for pain. Pure negligence.

Joe and Gary exchange a knowing look that means they could have a possible target for this documentary, which increases Gary's interest.

Joe: It would be hard to prove negligence from here.

Mary Lake Day: Oh, I already have the proof.

Mary hands Joe a folded short letter that Joe opens and reads quickly.

Joe: How did you get this?

Mary Lake Day: She brought it to me about a year after Larayne died.

Joe: May I make a copy of this?

*****

Later, at the same motel, the parking lot is nearly empty except for the Bingham van and the crew vehicles parked outside the same motel room.

127

In the motel's registration lobby, Gary, with his writing folder on the counter, finishes registering for a room and hands the motel owner his credit card.

Gary: I'd like a room for two with two beds with a senior discount. We don't know how long we'll be here.

Motel Owner (swipes & returns card): Yes, sir. Forty-nine dollars per night plus tax.

Gary sees the copy machine and takes the room key from the motel owner.

Gary: Could I pay you to make a copy of this letter?

*****

In Bob and Joe's motel room, Kansas and Kenny sit on chairs talking with Joe and Bob, who are stretched out on beds as if watching TV with heads pillowed against the headboard. Joe has an open file beside him. A KNOCK on the door, then Kansas lets Gary in. Gary hands the room key to Kansas.

Gary (points for Kansas): Next room down.

Kansas (to Gary): How much do we owe you?

Gary (waves it off): Forget it.

Kansas (confused): You sure?

Gary nods yes with forced courtesy smile.

Kenny (grins at Gary): Yeah, thanks Gary.

Kansas: I'm going to grab a shower.

Gary (to Kansas): Can I get a copy of today's work?

Kansas: I have some editing to do. I'll have it to you by breakfast.

Gary: Great.

After Kansas leaves the room, Gary takes her seat.

Gary (to Joe): I got a copy of that letter.

Joe: Good.

Joe gets up and paces the room while talking to the crew.

Joe (to Gary): Bob found out that the then-RN, Judith Blanchard, sent Mary that note about her sister's care.

Gary nods positively.

Joe (to Gary): She works right here in Lincoln at the nursing home's corporate headquarters. (closer to Gary) They manage dozens of facilities in the Midwest. (in front of Gary) You know what this means?

Gary: Two targets in one location.

Joe (kneels down to Gary): And … you've got to target the right one.

Gary: Maybe this Judith Blanchard doesn't have the resources to be a target.

Joe: Maybe if you target the suits, they could stall for years and not even care about your documentary.

Joe removes a form from his file on the bed and gives it to Gary.

Joe: Mary wants her two shares to go to her Disabled Vets. Her lawyer will distribute the money for her.

Gary: So, I get a share and Kenny and Kansas split a share?

Joe: Right. (thinks) If you use this ex-RN's letter to target the suits, they'll fire her for sure.

Gary: She might be a suit. That's your call, Gary.

Bob (stretched out on bed): Or, maybe the suits fire her and call your bluff. Not caring about your documentary. One fish in a big pond to them. This is a big target.

Joe stretches out on his bed.

Joe (to Gary): I'd say go to the nurse first and find out what she knows. All she said in the letter is that she knows the staff was negligent in administering Larayne's meds.

Bob: Maybe a documentary is the only way to go on this one.

Kenny (to Bob & Joe): So we can stay here while you're here?

Bob (knowing grin to Joe): That's the plan.

Joe grins back at Bob, gets up from the bed with the file and hands the file to Gary, who prefers an easy target to a documentary any day because of the marketing he'd have to do.

Gary (reading file): So how much for this target?

Joe: I'll leave this one up to you, Gary.

*****

That night, in Bob and Joe's motel room, Kenny and Joe enjoy their MUTED conversation as Bob has fallen asleep watching TV as:

Kansas is asleep in one of the two queen-size beds in adjoining motel room as:

Lights are off in Traveller on the motel parking lot as Gary lies on Traveller's upper berth thinking back to that awful time he lost his mother to hospital negligence.

{GARY'S FLASHBACK}:

It's 2002 in a hospital intensive care unit as Gary, now 48, kisses goodbye his elderly COMATOSE MOTHER on life support and exits the area sobbing.

{END OF GARY'S FLASHBACK}

In Traveller, Gary turns on the berth's overhead light, hops out of bed, gets a root beer from the fridge and starts writing under a light on the couch with one leg elevated.

*****

SERIES OF SHOTS:

It's dawn the next morning at the same rural Nebraska motel as the Joni Mitchell song "Both Sides Now" begins and plays throughout this series of shots as Gary exits Traveller in his robe and slippers, carrying his shaving kit toward Kansas and Kenny's room. He knocks on their motel room door. Bleary-eyed Kansas opens the door to let Gary in to grab a shower.

Later, in an office reception area, Gary is dressed to meet his possible target wearing a business suit with his briefcase and laptop case nearby; he waits for executive JUDITH BLANCHARD, 45-50, Caucasian, who comes out to greet Gary. They shake hands and Gary follows her into her executive office.

Later, in Blanchard's office, Judith finishes watching MUTED Mary Lake Day interview on facility parking lot with Disabled Vets supporting her. Gary closes his laptop, opens his briefcase and hands Blanchard a copy of her letter she gave to Mary Lake Day. Then Gary hands her a copy of his proposal that she reads with keen interest. Gary excuses himself and leaves her office with his briefcase and laptop in hand as she reads his proposal.

Outside the executive home office building, as the song continues, Gary exits the building, unbuttons his top shirt button, loosens his tie and breathes deeply after giving the target his proposal. He walks to the Jeep, gets behind the wheel and drives away.

Gary drives the red Jeep on a rural Nebraska highway as the song continues:

In the facility dining hall, Bob and Mary Lake Day sit across from each other chatting and laughing at a table in the otherwise empty room as:

In Warden Ellen's office, Joe and Warden Ellen watch and listen to a live interview between Inmate Trainee #2 and a FEMALE INMATE as Kansas stands behind a camera.

In a Lincoln mall game room, Kenny plays a video game as:

In same rural motel parking lot, the Jeep is parked near Shasta and Traveller as Gary naps in boxers and T-shirt on Traveller's couch with one leg elevated as the song fades out.

END SERIES OF SHOTS.

*****

At dusk, outside the same motel, Joe, dressed in civilian clothes, HEARS Traveller's bathroom fan running before he knocks on Traveller's screen door with its window shade pulled down. Gary, still in boxers and T-shirt opens his screen door. Gary is stoned.

Gary (off screen): What's up?

Joe: We're going out to eat! (smiles) Kenny's buying!

Gary opens the screen door for Joe and Joe steps up inside Traveller. Gary puts on pants and a shirt.

Joe: Did you meet with Blanchard?

Gary: She watched the documentary. I gave her a copy of her letter and left my proposal.

Joe (impressed): You decided to target her.

Gary (getting dressed): I know those corporate nursing home chains. And I know this documentary wouldn't move them to pay six figures. They'd rather pay a lawyer to deal with me. (wary of Joe) So I proposed fifty grand to drop the documentary, and it all goes to Mary's Disabled Vets. And she must make sure that any of the negligent staff has been fired.

Joe (smiles): You're a good man, Gary. I'll tell Kansas about it. I'm sure Kenny will be okay with it, too.

*****

Meanwhile, in the same mall game room, Kenny finishes his game and leaves.

On the Lincoln mall parking lot, Kenny gets into his car. Someone is watching Kenny's every move from a parked vehicle we don't see. Kenny gets his stash and pipe from his console, takes a deep hit just as an unmarked police car parks behind Kenny with flashers on. Kenny rolls down his window to exhale when POLICE OFFICER approaches Kenny with his badge visible.

Detective: Get out of the car!

Kenny (to self): Shit.

*****

133

Later, handcuffed Kenny is fingerprinted in police station booking area. That night, Kenny's Mustang is towed out of mall parking lot as: In local restaurant, the crew, minus Kenny, enjoy their meal. Kansas and Gary sit across from Bob and Joe.

Joe (to Kansas): I told him it was his turn to buy dinner. I don't know why he's not here.

Kansas: Dad, don't worry about him. You're the one in jail.

They all laugh, except Joe.

*****

Later, in a police holding cell, Kenny looks depressed sitting on a cot in a dark holding cell area while incarcerated men in adjoining cells moan and groan from intoxication.

*****

SERIES OF SHOTS:

Joe wakes up in the middle of the night, unable to sleep. Joe gets out of bed and looks out from behind the curtained window to see that Kenny's car is not there.

Kansas is also awake in bed in her room. She sees the time and calls Kenny's cell phone. After no answer she closes her phone.

Back to the holding cell, Kenny can't sleep; he's lying on a cot staring at the ceiling. He's terrified of his surroundings and feels physically threatened for the first time in his life.

Having breakfast in a rural café the next morning, the crew minus Kenny eat a somber breakfast as again Kansas calls Kenny's number on her cell phone and no answer.

In a courtroom, haggard Kenny stands before a JUDGE, who fines Kenny five hundred dollars for possession of marijuana.

In clerk's office, Kenny gives the CLERK his debit card and gets a receipt for his fine.

Outside a towing business, tired Kenny gets out of a cab after paying the driver. Kenny walks toward the towing business office knowing this has been the second worst time of his life.

In Warden Ellen's office, Joe and the warden watch an inmate trainee's interview on a monitor as Joe takes notes. Bob discreetly makes a cell phone call and we see on split screen a POLICE OFFICER talking to Bob in MUTED conversation. We can see on the police officer's computer screen: Kenny Long's arrest for marijuana possession.

Kenny is tired, driving his car after his ordeal. He picks up his cell phone from his car's console and doesn't check his messages.

END SERIES OF SHOTS

*****

Later, on the facility parking lot, a new Buick parks, whereupon Judith Blanchard, Gary's new target, gets out of her vehicle wearing a business suit. She locks her purse and briefcase in the trunk of her car before walking toward the prison's front entrance.

A bit later, in the facility's family visitor's area, Judith, seated alone at a private table, watches Mary Lake Day approach her, escorted by a female corrections officer. Mary sits across the table from Judith. The officer leaves them alone. Mary is a compassionate listener. Mary has never met Judith, since Judith's letter was not delivered in person. MUTE introduction then:

> Judith Blanchard (sincerely): I'm so sorry for the loss of your sister.

Mary extends her hand to Judith and they hold hands from across the table.

Judith Blanchard: I was working the night shift at the Omaha home where Larayne lived. I witnessed this LPN named Marcia Davis over-filling your sister's prescription at the Nurse's Station. I followed her to your sister's room, not believing what I was seeing. Davis was taking meds from your sister's med cups and stuffing them into her pocket, uncaring to how many pills were left for your sister. It was all so shocking. (beat) Now here comes the shameful part. I had just interviewed for this corporate executive position in Lincoln. I knew if I said anything about this to anyone I'd be making waves for my big promotion.

Mary's compassion causes Judith to cover her trembling mouth.

Judith (composes self): I did get that promotion. (beat) As soon as I could, I made sure that Marcia Davis was fired by her shift supervisor. When I found out later that Davis was working in a home we didn't own, I made a call to that facility to alert them. It was at this time I found out your sister had died a few weeks after I'd left. (more tears) I'm so sorry, Mary.

Mary pats Judith's hand as Judith removes an envelope from her suit jacket and hands it to Mary. Mary opens the envelope and removes a certified check made out to her for fifty thousand dollars. Mary is stunned.

Judith Blanchard: This won't bring back Larayne. Mr. Fleming said it's for you to give to your Disabled Vets.

Mary squeezes Judith's hand, elated with this generous gesture.

*****

Later, at the same rural Nebraska motel, Kenny's Mustang is parked in front of his room as the crew arrives after working all day at the facility. The crew meets at Kenny's door. Kansas uses her key to open the door with Joe right with her. Bob and Gary wait outside the room.

In Kansas and Kenny's motel room, Kenny is asleep on top of the bedspread; he's wearing only a bath towel after a shower. Joe stops Kansas from saying anything to wake her brother, ushering her gently and quietly back out of the room and closing the door quietly behind them.

Outside their motel rooms, Kansas understands that Kenny needs sleep. She and Gary walk over to Shasta and Traveller. Bob pulls his uniform shirt out from his pants before he unlocks his motel room door.

Bob (discreetly to Joe): You think he'll tell you he got busted?

Joe: No. (smiles) I wouldn't.

Bob chuckles while he unlocks their motel room door and they go inside.

Inside their room, Bob and Joe stretch out on their beds with their arms folded in front of them while propped up by pillows against the headboards.

Bob: Brother Joseph?

Joe (thinking about Kenny): Yeah?

Bob: Your son is not busy enough. Way too much idle time for that boy.

Joe: I know.

Bob (recounts): He plays video games for hours, comes out of the mall, gets into his car, hits his pipe, an unmarked car sees him, arrests him for possession, and he spends the night in jail.

Joe (negative shaking of head): I know. I know. You're right. They fine him five hundred bucks, impound his car. He had to pay a couple hundred to get his car back.

Bob: It's been a costly lesson for Kenny Long.

Joe (positive nod): Yeah.

Bob: That's a big do-Dad.

Joe: What do you mean?

Bob: What are you gonna do, Dad?

Joe: He's eighteen. I'm not going to do anything.

Bob: He's got to be smart. You don't smoke and carry weed in your vehicle.

Joe: I'm sure he knows that now.

Bob: Amen. (changes subject) You going to tell Kansas and Gary what happened?

Joe: No. They know he screwed up and missed interviews. Kenny can tell them if he wants. (looks at clock) Let's let him sleep till seven.

Bob: I can't eat that late.

Joe: So, we'll go for a walk after we eat.

Bob (nods no): No. No. Who's in charge here? This ain't one of your files, Brother Joseph.

Joe: What are you talking about?

Bob: I'm talkin' 'bout when we go to dinner.

Joe: Okay boss, what's your plan?

*****

It's early evening, Kansas's Jeep is gone when Joe exits his room and knocks on Kenny's door. Kenny stirs in bed, gets up after Joe knocks louder. Tired Kenny has a towel around his waist. Kenny opens the door and Joe enters as Kenny heads for the bathroom. Joe lies back on the other bed as Kenny uses the bathroom then splashes water on his face at the sink before finger-combing his hair after his long nap.

Kenny: What time is it?

Joe: Seven, and time for dinner … just you and me. The others left for dinner an hour ago. You hungry?

*****

Later, in a rural café, seated at a booth, Joe watches Kenny eat like a hungry wolf.

Joe: What happened last night?

Kenny (eating): I got busted for possession. Some cop in an unmarked car saw me take a hit from my pipe. It's been a real learning experience, Dad. I experienced this intense physical vulnerability in a holding cell.

Joe: They kept you overnight?

Kenny nods yes while eating.

Kenny: This morning I went before a judge who fined me five hundred bucks. Then I had to take a cab over to a towing company to get my car back. That was another hundred and ninety bucks. And they took my weed.

Joe (eating): Rough night.

Kenny nods in agreement while eating.

139

Kenny: All night I kept hearing these men in other holding cells, and I thought about you and how you've been locked up for twelve years. It was scary and humbling, Dad. (beat) I've decided to slow down on the weed and get into MMA.

Joe: Mixed martial arts.

Nods yes while eating.

Kenny: They have the best training. I know this MMA gym a few miles from our house. Donna "The Bell" Snyder trains there.

Joe: That's Jimmy Snyder's daughter. He's in Bingham.

Kenny (stunned): Really? You know her father?

Joe (eating): I've interviewed him. I know his daughter sends him tickets to her fights.

Kenny: Really?

Joe nods yes while eating.

Joe: Why the sudden interest in MMA?

Kenny chooses his words carefully.

Kenny: Last night I got scared that I couldn't handle myself if I had to. It's not a good feeling.

Joe gives his understanding nod, knowing Kenny's been raised by his sister.

Joe (upbeat): I think this MMA training would be good for you. It would help you get in shape. That's always a confidence builder. (beat) I was never a fighter. (smiles) Plenty of times I wished I was. You're at that age where certain guys test you.

Kenny: Yeah, they screw with you.

Joe: Right. And you're also right that it sucks to feel like you can't handle yourself. Hell, I still come across that every day. (changes subject) Before I forget, Gary pitched the target yesterday, and today the target delivered fifty grand to Mary Lake Day. It all goes to her Disabled Vets.

Kenny: Sweet.

Joe: I want you to know that Gary gave all four shares to them on his own.

Kenny: That's cool. Those people need it more than we do.

Joe smiles at his son as they enjoy a meal alone.

*****

Meanwhile, Kansas has made Kenny's bed; she's reading on her motel room bed when there's a knock on her door. She sees Gary and lets him in.

Gary: You reading?

Kansas (book in hand): Yeah.

Gary: I wanted to talk to you about Kenny.

Kansas (sits on bed): Okay.

Gary (paces): I don't know what happened to Kenny and it isn't a big deal in the grand scheme of things. I mean, hell, he's a recreational user like I am. But, do you think I influence him in a deleterious way that might contribute to how much he smokes?

Kansas: Deleterious?

Gary (stops pacing): Do you think I'm a bad or negative influence on Kenny?

Kansas: No. Whatever happened ... it's Kenny's life.

Gary: Yeah. (beat) I'll let you get back to your book.

Kansas: Gary, you can stay and watch TV if you want. It won't bother me. It's your room, too.

Gary: Well, okay. Maybe I'll watch something until Kenny gets back.

Kansas goes back to reading as Gary takes off his shoes, grabs remote and surfs MUTED TV while stretched out on Kenny's bed.

*****

Meanwhile, in the same mall game room, Kenny and Joe play partners, each playing a flipper during a pinball game. They're having a great time.

*****

Back to Kansas and Kenny's motel room, Gary turns off the TV with the remote and stares at the blank screen.

Kansas (stops reading): You okay, Gary?

Gary (looks at Kansas): I got this sudden urge to go see my dad. He's eighty and lives in his Airstream in this Yuma RV park on the bank of the Colorado River.

Kansas: Is your mother still alive?

Gary: No, she died about twelve years ago.

Kansas: So your dad's been alone since then?

Gary: No, they divorced when I was a boy.

Kansas: Who raised you?

142

Gary sits up on the side of the bed with his feet on the floor and facing Kansas.

Gary: They both did. I lived with my mom until after the ninth grade and then my dad till I graduated from high school.

Kansas: In Yuma?

Gary: Phoenix. My dad used to live there. My mother lived in Tucson. (beat) Right after I pitched this last target I realized I missed my mom. She died from hospital negligence.

Kansas: Like Mary Lake Day's sister?

Gary: Sort of. (beat) Kansas, I wanted to ask you if you'd be open to interviewing me and my dad in Yuma … doing a Living Legacy?

Kansas puts her book down, thinking about going to Yuma with Gary and leaving her brother alone.

Gary: I'd pay you and cover all expenses. How about if I paid you a grand for an edited Living Legacy with my dad?

Kansas: It would be the first time Kenny was home alone without me.

Gary: He's eighteen now ... and comes home when he wants.

Kansas isn't as amused as Gary.

Gary: Sorry. Bad joke. (beat) Maybe the time alone would be good for him. He needs to grow up like every kid his age.

Gary watches Kansas thinking about it.

Kansas: A grand and you pay expenses?

Gary nods yes.

Kansas: I'd go if you pull Shasta. I like my own bed.

Gary: Sure. Shasta's not that heavy. My dad's place has clean restrooms with showers and laundry. You could drive his old truck around Yuma. And you could use it all you want.

Kansas: We'd be gone a week?

Gary: Ten days at the most.

Kansas: Okay.

Gary claps his hands together then high-fives Kansas.

Kansas: And as long as Joe doesn't need us.

Gary: Joe told me we're laying low for a few weeks. The timing's perfect.

Kansas: We'll talk to Joe and Kenny tomorrow.

Gary: This is good news. I'm out of here. Good night.

Gary exits the motel room, leaving Kansas with thoughts about going to Yuma and leaving Kenny home alone for the first time since she came back to get him when he was six. That's why Kansas feels conflicted.

*****

NEXT DAY

 In Warden Ellen's office area, Kenny is manning a camera pointed at inmate trainee #3 and a FEMALE INMATE, as Joe and Bob watch the interview with inmate trainees 1 & 2. Warden Ellen comes over to Joe to let him know he has a phone call and hands Joe her cell phone.

Warden Ellen: It's Warden Ted.

144

Joe (on cell phone): Hey, Warden.

Warden Ted (off screen on phone): Hey, Joe! Warden Ellen is really happy with what you've set up there. She tells me there's a positive energy buzz in her facility that she hasn't experienced until now. You know how that makes me feel, Mr. Long?

Joe (on phone): No, sir.

Warden Ted (off screen on phone): It gives me hope for the future in a business where hope can get lost. (changes subject) I want you and Bob back here for lunch in my office tomorrow at noon. The governor is coming here later tomorrow afternoon. He wants to meet with you. I know this is short notice, but this is a big deal to The Corporation.

Joe is stunned. He can only manage to say:

Joe (dazed on phone): Tomorrow at noon. Bye, sir.

*****

That night, in Bob and Joe's motel room, Joe paces the room talking to the crew.

Joe: I'm happy with the way things are going. I want to thank you all for doing good work here. (beat) We'll lay low for a while. It's good timing for Kansas and Gary to go to Yuma to visit Gary's father. And Kenny plans to get in shape. We leave early tomorrow. Good night.

Kansas, Gary and Kenny leave Bob and Joe's room. Kansas unlocks her door, leaving the door ajar for Kenny as Kansas goes into her room.

Gary (to Kenny): I just wanted to say we couldn't do this without you. And anytime you need to talk about anything, I'll listen.

Kenny smiles, hugs Gary and goes into his room. Gary walks toward Traveller.

*****

NEXT DAY

In a Wichita mixed martial arts training center, DONNA "THE BELL" SNYDER, 19, attractive Caucasian, 135-lb. bantam-weight MMA fighter, is in the throes of training hard when her trainer, TRAINER CORY, 30-35 male Caucasian, walks up to his fighter. Donna sees good news in her trainer's eyes.

> Donna: We got it?

Cory smiles and nods yes, whereupon they embrace joyfully. Then he grabs each shoulder of his top fighter, an undefeated rising star close to getting a UFC contract.

> Trainer Cory (soft intensity): Let this stick to your brain: You got only three weeks to get ready for Wanda "The Beast" Crawford, a top twenty contender. She wants to beat an undefeated fighter on your turf.

> Donna (excited): The fight's here?

> Trainer Cory: That's right. Crawford's unbeaten in twenty-one fights. She loves to ground and pound. We'll work on your take-down defense. Core work, I want increased fifty percent. You'll spar every day for the next three weeks. Got it?

Donna nods yes and goes back to her training.

> Trainer Cory: Donna? You still don't have a manager?

She shakes her head no.

> Trainer Cory: You better get one. After you beat Crawford you're in the top twenty. A good manager will get you top dollar

146

with incentives and a UFC contract. (smiles) And more money for your trainer.

Donna smiles back at her trainer then gets back to her tough workout regimen for her upcoming fight as:

We hear a desk phone RING and follow it to Trainer Cory's office. We listen to the message Kenny leaves as:

On the Bingham parking lot, Kansas reads in her parked Jeep as Kenny leans on his Mustang to deliver a message on his cell phone to the MMA trainer.

Kenny (on cell phone): Cory, this is Kenny Long. I'm interested in training at your gym. Wanted to find out the details. Or I can stop by tomorrow. Yeah, I'll stop in tomorrow. Bye.

Kenny puts away his cell phone, inserts his iPod earbud and listens to Robert Palmer singing "Bad Case of Loving You" as he stares up at Bingham's distant guard tower.

End of Episode 3

Episode 4:

Bad Case

E arly morning in a Yuma, Arizona, shaded RV park, Kansas
and Gary sit on the bank of the Colorado River having
coffee. Not far behind them is an older-model silver
Airstream travel trailer parked in its space near unattached
Traveller and Shasta. An old pickup is parked by the Airstream.
Gary and Kansas have been here five days and their agendas are in
conflict:

Kansas: Okay, I have to say this. Before we left Wichita you
promised you'd have me back home for Kenny's birthday this
Friday. I know Joe has a big birthday surprise for him. Gary, we
have to shoot today and leave in the morning in order to be back by
Friday. That was the deal, Gary.

Gary: I know. I know. We'll shoot today.

Kansas: With your dad.

Gary: With my dad.

Kansas: Good. And we'll leave in the morning.

Gary: We leave in the morning.

Kansas: Good.

Gary dreads doing the interview with his cranky father as:

148

From an open window in the Airstream, ARNIE FLEMING, 80, Caucasian, moves away from his open window after hearing his son and Kansas talking outside. Arnie is a retired veteran, fiercely independent, living on social security and the money Gary sends him. Gary is a good son. Arnie thinks his son is a hack writer. Gary and now Kansas know that Arnie is an alcoholic with early signs of dementia. Arnie is paranoid because he knows his son wants to film him in order to show he's mentally ill and should live in a care facility. Kansas does not know that Gary lured her out here on the pretense of a Living Legacy interview; instead Gary wants documented proof that his father cannot continue living alone. This is a tough time for Gary too, because he loves his father.

*****

Meanwhile, in a Wichita MMA gym, Kenny feels out of place working out with these fit and flexible young male and female MMA STUDENTS while looking at a poster-size photo on the gym wall of Donna "The Bell" Snyder in fight pose, the same poster he bought for his bedroom wall yesterday.

*****

Next morning, at the crew's new rental house in the country, the Mustang and Jeep are parked on the large graveled parking area.

Kenny's alarm clock goes off, playing "Sunshine" by Atmosphere. Kenny wakes in his new king-size bed; his body is sore after his MMA workout. He hobbles into the bathroom. We can see the same MMA poster of Donna on his bedroom wall as:

*****

Warden Ted is seated behind his desk across from Bob and Joe. The warden presents Joe with a gift for the work Joe did at the women's prison in Nebraska: a laptop with carrying case.

149

Joe (confused): I can use this, in here?

Warden Ted: Anywhere you want in Bingham.

Bob (clarifying): So Warden, Joe can take this laptop anywhere in Bingham?

Warden Ted (smiles): That's right.

Joe: So I can email anybody outside Bingham?

The warden smiles, nodding his head yes.

Bob (more clarifying): But we will have access to everything incoming and outgoing, and everything he receives and sends out?

Another smiling, affirmative nod from the warden.

Joe: Warden, why are you doing this?

The affable warden sits back in his chair.

Warden Ted: The three of us arrived at Bingham around the same time. Bob, you told me that Joe was interviewing inmates like a journalist, getting valuable information from a lot of directions. (to Bob) You remember that?

Bob: Yes, sir.

Warden Ted (to Joe): The Corporation and I know that you are saving lives out there by doing what you do in here. You have personally interviewed at my request every inmate who was about to be released or up for parole. Not one of those inmates that were released on your recommendation has returned to us or any other correctional facility. I want this laptop used wisely over the next eight years, getting your system organized and replicated in other facilities. (to Bob) Officer Fuller, you get this man anything he needs to get this going.

Joe: Warden, if I could get access to inmate files, this could be really helpful.

Bob: Sir, I believe with access to files we could do a better job screening the inmates we train to be interviewers.

Joe nods in agreement.

Warden Ted: I'll call Denver today.

Joe: Oh, Warden, there's one favor I need in order to really get this running smooth.

Bob: And Warden, I'm with him again on this one.

Warden Ted (smiles): Anything. What is it?

*****

Friday night in a Wichita sports arena; it's Kenny's 19th birthday. Joe, in civilian clothes, is seated next to Kenny in the front row; they're watching the end of a women's MMA fight in the cage before the main event fight with small FIGHT CROWD in attendance. Bob, in civilian clothes, sits behind Joe. Kenny holds the fight card brochure as the fight ends.

Kenny (to Joe): I can't believe you're here with me on my birthday! (beat) Dad, I hope you don't mind I had Kansas show me Jimmy Snyder's file.

Joe: No, I think it's cool how you took Jimmy's favorite song and emailed his daughter to play it for her pre-fight song! We're all impressed!

Bob (into Kenny's ear): Donna "The Bell" Snyder ... one hundred and thirty-five pounds of pure tiger.

Kenny: Why do they call her "The Bell"?

Joe (to Kenny): Wait till it rings...

Joe & Bob: You'll find out!

Joe and Bob laugh. Robert Palmer sings "Bad Case Of Loving You" on the arena sound system as DONNA SNYDER, Caucasian, 19, undefeated 135-lb. MMA fighter with a chip on her shoulder, walks out toward the cage and then stops for inspection by FIGHT OFFICIAL and REFEREE. Kenny is mesmerized with her. Donna enters the cage and sees the men sitting in her reserved seats for her father and dead mother as her pre-fight song stops. Donna's opponent, WANDA "THE BEAST" CRAWFORD, 25-30, African American MMA veteran fighter, is soon ready. Then: the bell RINGS, whereupon Donna knocks Wanda out with a head kick in 10 seconds. The crowd goes wild and Trainer Cory embraces his fighter in the ring. The fight is over in record time.

Bob (in Kenny's ear): What did I tell you? Donna "The Bell" Snyder -

Joe: Two 'N's -

Bob: Two 'L's -

Joe (points to Kenny): Why do they call her "The Bell?"

Kenny & Bob: Wait till it rings ... you'll find out!

Kenny watches Donna leave the cage after the referee raises her arm in victory. Kenny has a crush on this rising MMA star.

*****

Later, outside the women's locker room in the arena, Bob and Joe stand together chatting as Kenny leans against the women's locker room wall listening to Robert Palmer sing "Bad Case of Loving You" on his iPod with earbud inserted.

Bob (messing with Kenny): Birthday Boy?

152

Kenny removes his earbud.

Bob: What are you going to say to "The Bell" when she comes out?

Just then: Donna exits the women's locker room with her gym bag slung over her shoulder. Kenny calls out to her from behind her:

Kenny: I liked your pre-fight song!

Donna stops and turns back to Kenny.

Donna: How do you know my dad?

Kenny: I don't know him. (points to Joe) My dad knows your dad.

Donna (friendly to Joe): You're Joe Long. Are you out now?

Joe (smiles): Right now, yes I am.

Bob (to Donna): Your dad gave his tickets to Joe. It's Kenny's birthday.

Donna (to Kenny): Happy birthday.

Kenny: I have a birthday wish.

Donna (smiles): Yeah, what's that?

*****

Later, in an ice cream shop, Joe and Bob sit in a booth having ice cream. Kenny and Donna sit in a booth next to them. Bob and Kenny sit back-to-back within earshot as Bob eavesdrops on their conversation. Kenny and Donna are having licorice ice cream. Donna is curious about this guy Kenny, who shows up in her dad's seat after emailing her to play her dad's song for her pre-fight.

Donna (frankly): The only reason I'm here is out of respect for my dad and because we have something strange in common.

Kenny: I know. We both love licorice ice cream.

Donna laughs. She likes Kenny.

Kenny: I have to say that it's a bit humbling to have ice cream with a girl who can kick my ass.

Donna smiles while nodding in agreement.

Bob (discreet whisper to Joe): She likes him.

Kenny: We work out at the same gym.

She nods positively while eating ice cream.

Kenny (cuts to chase): You have a boyfriend?

Donna: No time for that.

Kenny: Really?

Donna: If you're talking relationship: No way. (beat) Look, I have to go.

Donna starts to get up to leave.

Kenny: I'm curious, who named you "The Bell'"?

Donna has to leave and walks out of the store. Kenny watches her get into her car and drive off.

Bob (off screen to Kenny): Her father gave her the name.

As Kenny sits in the same booth staring absently out the window:

Joe (off screen to Kenny): Jimmy Snyder was a fighter. Never went pro. He boxed in Kansas City gyms and was a Golden Gloves champ in his day.

Bob (nods in agreement): Jimmy was a good welterweight.

Kenny's still looking out the window; he's thinking about his next move with Donna.

*****

Later that night, outside the crew's rental house, the black unmarked Bingham prison van is parked near the crew's vehicles. Shasta is still hooked up to Traveller because Gary and Kansas returned home from Arizona just hours ago.

Inside the house, Kansas shows Joe how to use his new laptop at the dining room table, where Bob, Kenny, and Gary drink coffee with Kenny's birthday cake. Kansas and Gary have tans.

Bob (teasing): I think Kenny fell in love tonight.

Kansas: With who?

Bob: Donna "The Bell" Snyder.

Kansas (to Kenny): She's that girl on your poster.

Joe: An undefeated fighter.

Kansas (to Kenny): You like her?

Kenny: Wait a minute, people. I just met her. I happen to train at the same gym she does, that's all.

Gary and Bob laugh.

Kenny (to Gary & Bob): What's so funny about that?

Bob: You tell her trainer that her father - serving life for killing her mother - would like Donna to play his favorite song, "Bad Case of Loving You" before her fight tonight.

Gary (to Kenny): Then you show up at her fight in her dad's seat. That takes balls. I admire that.

Joe (to Kenny): Don't listen to them. It worked! She had ice cream with you for God's sake an hour after she KO'd her opponent in ten seconds of the first round! (beat) What I'd like to know is: what's your next move with "The Bell"?

Kenny is still working on that.

*****

NEXT DAY

Kenny gets out of his car with his gym bag and enters the same MMA gym.

Trainer Cory is behind the front desk doing paperwork.

Kenny: Congrats on the fight, Cory!

Trainer Cory: Thanks, man.

Kenny: Cory, I'd like to step up my training to another level, move away from the beginner's class. (pulls out wad of cash) You know what I mean?

Cory is more interested now.

*****

That night, in Joe's private cell, Joe sits at his desk under a desk lamp scanning the files of inmates on his laptop screen; he's looking for his crew's next target. We see him clicking through head-shots and data on inmates while making notes in his notebook.

156

*****

Gary sits alone writing after a meal in a quiet cafe. An inveterate loner, Gary likes going to a new place to write. A YOUNG WAITRESS comes over to Gary with a coffee pot.

Waitress: More coffee?

Gary: Please. (beat) Thanks.

Gary goes back to writing.

Gary (voice over writing): *I don't know what to think of this family I've fallen in with. The money is good and easy so far; and living with Kansas and Kenny is a bit awkward, since I'm old enough to be their father. For now at least, I'll stick around, to at least see if Kenny gets his butt kicked by his MMA girlfriend. This Donna "The Bell" Snyder is undefeated, a real killer fighter with early knockouts. Kenny and Donna have this bizarre thing in common: their fathers are doing time in Bingham for killing their mothers. I don't have to write any more novels, because I'm writing about our lives in this incredible independent film crew that makes positive things happen, such incredible things I dare not mention now. My father would only dismiss what I'm doing as "blackmail"; and that's exactly why I couldn't really talk to him about what I'm doing. He doesn't listen to me. So I don't listen to him. Two egos and zero connection, although we did have a breakthrough before we left Yuma. More about that later.*

Gary stops writing, puts away his writing stuff inside his black bag, and leaves cash on the table before exiting the cafe.

*****

NEXT DAY

At the same MMA gym, Kenny gets a private training session with trainer Cory, working out at a much higher level than out-of-shape Kenny.

*****

Same day, in Joe's private cell, Joe is seated at his desk in front of his laptop looking at a headshot of inmate GLEN MEAD, 40-45, Caucasian, former insurance claims adjuster. Joe thinks back to his interview with Mead six months ago:

{JOE'S FLASHBACK}:

Officer Bob stands guard outside Mead's cell during Joe's interview with Mead. Bob doesn't like Mead.

Joe leans against the cell wall taking notes as Mead anxiously paces the cell he shares with another inmate who's been moved for this private interview with Joe Long.

Mead (to Joe): How do I know you're not wired? Everyone in here knows you're just a spy and a snitch for the warden and your Uncle Tom out there.

Bob heard that remark and is not happy with Mead.

Joe (relaxed): I wouldn't tell you if I was wired.

Mead: I guess that's true.

Joe sits on one of the two twin-size beds as Mead paces his cell.

Joe: I'm not wired, Mead. I'll cut to the chase and tell you I know you assaulted your mother-in-law and she spent three months in the hospital. I did check on your story and I believe your mitigating circumstances. (reads file) You've served six years and come up for parole in six months. Your mother-in-law showed up at your last parole board hearing fearing your release, convincing the board to deny your release.

158

Mead (smart ass): I've heard how you work, Long. You want a target from me and you want to know if I'm a danger to anyone outside. (stops pacing to make point) And I didn't torch her house. (continues pacing) I punched her once and she was out cold. I left her house and her Thanksgiving turkey was in the oven and it smoke-damaged the interior of her house.

Joe (reads file): She was hospitalized for twelve weeks, on oxygen in intensive care for three weeks … and you broke her nose.

Mead: Yeah. So what?

Joe: You don't seem at all remorseful for any of her injuries.

Mead steps over to Joe because he doesn't want Bob to hear him.

Mead (angry whisper): Look, Joe, I'll tell you straight up what you need to do to make sure I don't kill that woman when I get out.

Mead sees Bob staring at him.

Mead (to Joe): But not here.

Joe: Where?

Mead: That private place where you get to write and smoke all you want. I want to finish this interview there and have a smoke with you.

Joe looks over at Bob, to see what Bob thinks about moving this jerk.

*****

Outside, Joe and Mead sit across from each other smoking at Joe's writing table. Joe is making notes in Mead's file as Bob waits nearby.

Joe (writing): I'm writing down the questions I want to ask you. Then I note your answer.

Mead: I'll do that sometimes. I'll have a visitor coming and I'll spend two weeks writing down the questions I want to ask. I hate forgetting things. My mother-in-law called me O.C.D.

Joe (writing): Isn't that what your mother-in-law was doing: messing with your mind?

Mead: Yes, and that is what she's still doing.

Joe (stops writing): How's that?

Mead: For starters: she shows up at my parole board hearing begging them not to let me out. She threatens to sue the state if I get out and cause her problems. (beat) My wife was a clone of her mother. Her mother moved into our house that she co-signed for and drove me crazy. I mean this woman talked my wife into making her the beneficiary of my wife's estate if anything happened to my wife. I hate that woman, Joe. She's been living in my house for six years while I'm in here.

Joe: Sounds like your wife isn't coming to bat for you.

Mead: She's my ex-wife now. She divorced me right away.

Joe: Sorry to hear that.

Mead: Not me, man.

Joe (reads file): Okay Mead, why is your mother-in-law a target?

Mead: I falsified, over-valued her belongings in our homeowner's policy I wrote myself. Mostly jewelry she said I stole after I punched her.

Joe (writing): How much over value?

Mead: At least four hundred grand.

Joe takes that in as if this could be a potential target.

Joe: And you can prove this?

Mead (leans closer): I can get the insurance company to go after her. But they won't until I'm out of here. I'll make a deal with them so they won't prosecute me.

Joe: If we go after her, Mead, who gets your share?

Mead (coy): I'll let you know. (beat) But my share can go to anyone but me?

Joe: That's right.

Joe is done here. He gets up from his private table, signaling Bob to get on his pager to signal for an officer to come out here. Joe gathers his things and starts walking away, going for a walk on the prison grounds.

Mead (to Joe): So are you going after her?

Joe (walking away): I'll let you know.

An officer hustles over to Bob and escorts Mead away.

Bob catches up with Joe and walks with him.

Bob (concerned): You're going to target this guy's mother-in-law?

Joe: It could be easy. We'll see what Gary thinks.

Bob: I don't like Mead. He more or less said he'd kill her if he gets out.

Joe: And he thinks you're an Uncle Tom.

Bob laughs, knowing his buddy hit the nail on the head why he doesn't like Mead.

*****

NEXT DAY

At the same MMA gym, Kenny is training alone outside; he's flipping over a massive tractor tire until he falls face-first onto the tire, exhausted. He turns over and Donna "The Bell" Snyder stands over him looking down and smiling at Kenny, who's breathing hard in his sweat-stained shirt.

Donna: We do have something awful in common, don't we?

Kenny: Yeah. This MMA training sucks.

She likes his quick wit and humor.

Kenny (on his back): Can I ask you a personal question?

Donna (curious): What?

Kenny: Have you ever beat up your boyfriend?

Donna (laughs): I don't have a boyfriend.

Kenny: Why not?

Donna: It's a distraction.

Kenny: I can see that. Except ... I'd call it a good distraction.

Donna smiles and starts to walk away toward her car.

Kenny: When's your next fight?

Donna (walking): Don't know yet.

Kenny: Can I get one of your dad's tickets for your next fight and film it?

Donna walks back to Kenny, who still lies on his back on the big tire.

Donna: Why would you want to do that?

Kenny: That's what I do. My sister and I make documentaries for this writer, G. K. Fleming. I've never shot a fight.

Donna (walks away): Get a ticket from my dad. I send him two tickets every fight.

Kenny: Who's the other ticket for?

Donna (stops & turns back): My mom.

They look at each other knowing they do have something awful in common. She walks back over to Kenny, intrigued by him.

Kenny (sincerely): It doesn't matter how or why. We lost both of them. And because of what they did … we're already bad, aren't we?

Donna nods in agreement.

Donna: I love my dad. I was a daddy's girl. I'm fighting to be something other than the orphan girl from Wichita.

Understanding nod from Kenny.

Kenny (changes subject): I want to offer you a business deal you can't refuse.

Donna: What's that?

Kenny: You go out with me on one dinner date if I can get your dad in his seat at your next fight.

Donna sits down on the tire and gets in Kenny's face to read his eyes.

Donna: Are you messing with me?

Kenny nods no, intimidated by her intensity.

Kenny: My dad can make it happen.

She gauges his eyes and sees fear and truth.

Donna (serious whisper): If you can do something incredible like that, bring my dad to my next fight ... (leans closer) ... you can have anything you want from me.

Kenny is stunned to silence and watches her walk away to her car and drive off as trainer Cory comes out clapping his hands:

Trainer Cory: Let's go, Kenny! Work!

Kenny gets up and continues lifting and pushing over the huge tractor tire.

*****

Later, at the crew's house, Kenny parks his Mustang, and gingerly walks into the house after his workout and encounter with Donna. Gary and Kansas are home. Kenny sits at the dinner table, exhausted; Kansas prepares dinner in the kitchen.

Kansas (from kitchen): How was the workout?

Kenny: Exhausting.

Kansas (in dining room): Yeah?

Kenny: I talked to that fighter, Donna Snyder.

Kansas (sits down): And?

164

Kenny: I asked her out.

Kansas (surprised): And?

Kenny: I kind of told her I'd do something crazy if she'd go out with me.

Kansas: What?

Kenny: That I'd get her dad to show up at her next fight.

Kansas thinks about it.

Kansas: Because your dad got to take you to a fight you think your dad can get Jimmy Snyder to her fight?

Kenny's guilty nod.

Kansas: How can you even ask your dad to do such a thing? This is not something we advertise, Kenny.

Kenny: I really like her, Kan. I'm trying to impress her. Shit, I've got nothing else going for me. She's so out of my league it's not funny.

Kansas: I think you better be real with her, Kenny. And Joe would not appreciate you asking him to impose on Warden Ted.

Kenny nods positively, knowing he screwed up.

Kenny: Is Gary in Traveller?

*****

Gary writes on Traveller's couch with one leg elevated when there's a knock on his back door.

Kenny: It's me!

Gary (still writing): Come in!

165

Kenny sits lengthwise at Traveller's table with his back to the window while waiting for Gary to stop writing.

Gary (writing): Be right with you.

Gary puts down his writing.

Gary: I just got this new file from Joe. It's a good one.

Kenny: Really?

Gary gets up from the couch to get a root beer from the fridge. He offers Kenny one.

Kenny: Sure.

Gary hands Kenny a root beer then stretches out on the couch with his cold drink.

Gary: So how's the MMA thing going?

Kenny: I talked to Donna today.

Gary: Donna "The Bell" Snyder. That's a brilliant marketing name for a fighter by the way. (beat) You quit smoking weed?

Kenny: For now. (beat) Actually I'm out.

Gary: Already?

Kenny: They took my weed when I got busted. As if you didn't know.

Gary: In Wichita?

Kenny: My dad didn't tell you?

Gary shakes his head no.

Gary: What happened?

166

Kenny: I took a hit from my pipe, an unmarked cop in Lincoln saw me, took me to jail.

Gary: In Lincoln. So that's what happened. How'd you get out?

Kenny: A judge fined me five hundred bucks the next morning. And a couple hundred to get my car back. (beat) Kansas doesn't know either?

Gary: I don't know. I don't think so.

Kenny: It was an awful experience.

Gary (sudden dawning): That's why you got into MMA: You were afraid you'd get your butt kicked in jail!

Kenny: Don't tell Kansas. I don't need her hounding me.

Gary: I won't tell her.

Kenny: Thanks. (changes subject) Gary, I was working out and Donna came over to me and we talked. She's so tough. I don't know why I'm attracted to her when she could kick my ass. (beat) Gary, I told her I could get her dad to show up at one of her fights.

Gary: Are you kidding me? You can't ask Joe to get her dad out of there. It's taking advantage of Joe's arrangement with the warden.

Kenny (contrite): I know, I know. I just want her to go out with me.

Gary: You're trying to impress her.

Kenny nods in agreement.

Gary (curious): Tell me something: How do you plan on getting her dad to her fight?

Kenny: That's what I wanted to ask you. How could I?

Gary gets up to pace, shaking his head no at the notion until:

Gary: I'll think on it. No promises.

Kenny (perks up): Thanks, Gary. I got nothing. So anything you can come up with. (beat) I never asked you about your interview with your dad. How'd that go?

Gary (from couch): It was different. My dad has dementia. His brain is pickled from a half century of drinking every day. (paces while venting) It's too late for him. Too much damage done. My plan was to have Kansas film one of his episodes and commit him to the Yuma V.A.'s assisted living quarters, actually some real nice little cottages.

Kenny: What happened?

Gary (fake grin): I'd say he convinced me otherwise.

Kansas (off screen from house): Kenny! Gary! Time to eat!

They exit Traveller. As Gary and Kenny walk toward the house they talk.

Kenny: Tell me about this new case.

Gary: This inmate Mead punches his mother-in-law out for ruining his life. I can't blame the guy when you know what this woman did.

They enter the house. Gary and Kenny serve themselves in the kitchen from the stove and take their seats at the dinner table. They start to chat about the new case until Kansas, seated at the head of the table, does not want to hear about work right now.

Kansas: Guys, please. Let's eat now and discuss work after we eat, okay?

168

The men nod in agreement and begin eating.

Kansas (to Gary): I finished your interview with your dad.

Gary: Good. Thanks.

Kenny: I'd like to see that interview.

Gary (eating): I want to watch it alone first.

Kansas gives her brother a look that says it all, since she and Gary were at odds in Yuma for most of their visit with Arnie, Gary's dad.

Kenny: Oh, okay.

Gary (to Kenny): How much is it worth to you if I can come up with a plan for you and Donna?

Kansas (curious): What plan?

Kenny (to Kansas & Gary): I don't think we should discuss my business while we're eating.

Kansas is not amused with her brother's cavalier attitude. Gary and her brother's snickering angers Kansas as they eat in silence.

*****

That evening, Gary studies the file of their next target on Traveller's couch when Kenny knocks lightly on Traveller's open door.

Kenny: It's me!

Gary: Come in!

Kenny sits down at the table with his back against the wall.

Kenny: Half my share of the next case.

Gary (sits up): You sure about that?

Kenny: Yeah.

Gary gets up and paces up and down the aisle of Traveller, motivated by Kenny's offer.

Gary: When's her next fight?

Kenny: Her trainer says less than three weeks.

Gary: In Wichita?

Kenny: Yeah.

Gary: That helps. (beat) So if I can get her dad... What's his name?

Kenny: Jimmy Snyder.

Gary: So if I can get this Jimmy Snyder to attend his daughter's next fight you'll give me half of your share and it comes out of the next case when the target pays?

Kenny: That's right. (beat) Oh! And you can't tell anybody about half my share going to you if you do this. I don't want Joe or my sister knowing about it.

Gary: I agree, I think that's best.

Kenny: Any ideas yet?

Gary stretches out on the couch with one leg elevated.

Gary: I'll let you know.

Kenny leaves Traveller. Gary picks up the file of the new case and we see a black and white pic of Doris Newman, 60-65, Caucasian mother-in-law of inmate Mead and possibly Gary's next target.

*****

170

NEXT DAY

Kenny and Kansas film Gary and inmate Mead's interview for Gary's documentary at Joe's writing table. Gary sits across the table from Mead with notes in front of him. Bob and Joe watch the interview nearby as a director and producer would watch a scene.

Gary (follows script): What's the name of the insurance company you worked for?

Mead (on camera): Mutual Fidelity of Kansas.

Bob (off screen): Mu Fok insurance?

Kansas (off screen): I can edit that out.

Gary (to Mead): And you have a copy of the original policy you wrote, listing Doris Newman's jewelry and other valuables?

Mead (on camera): That's right.

Gary: What is the difference between the actual value of Mrs. Newman's alleged stolen jewelry and your appraised value on the policy?

Mead: Two hundred grand.

Gary (confused): I have to ask you why you didn't reveal this inflated appraisal to your employer since in your trial you were convicted of assault and robbery for jewelry you over-appraised by two hundred thousand dollars? Your mother-in-law, Doris Newman, pressed charges and she was paid two hundred grand over the appraised value of her jewelry. Help me understand why you wouldn't at least want to take that money away from the woman who sent you here for six years?

Mead: Mr. Fleming, Doris Newman knew I would never go to my employer. Because she also knew that Mutual Fidelity is owned by A. J. Wyatt, one extremely tight taskmaster is what I'd call him.

171

A. J. stands for "asshole jerk" for anyone who ever worked for Mr. Wyatt. My mother-in-law knew that if my boss went after me he'd make sure I never saw daylight until he was dead at the very least. He's known to be like a mafia boss when it comes to loyalty from employees. Don't ever break that trust. (beat) I can't get back six years. But I can get two hundred grand for my time. (beat) Doris and my ex-wife have to know where her jewelry is, because I didn't take it.

Gary: What guarantee does Doris Newman have that if she pays me two hundred grand for this little documentary that the matter is closed?

Mead: If I go to A. J. Wyatt with this information I can trade my immunity from further prosecution and he'll go after her and give me a reward when she's prosecuted. I want to let my old life and the house go. I'll move out west and start over. She could also turn me into Wyatt and for the rest of my life he'd make my life as miserable as possible.

Gary: What about your ex-wife?

Mead (testy): What about her?

Gary: You imply she was involved in the missing jewelry.

Mead: That's right.

Gary: Can you prove that?

Mead: I don't have to. I know her mother made two hundred grand off me and I can prove that.

Gary: So Doris has to decide if paying you is worth all the trouble you'll cause if she doesn't buy this documentary?

Mead: That's right. There's one more thing I want Doris to do. I want her to go to my parole board hearing and testify on my behalf.

Gary ends the interview. Bob escorts Mead back into the prison. Joe and Gary shake hands after the interview.

*****

Later, in the vast Bingham dining room, Kansas and Kenny sit across from Joe and Gary at a table in the empty dining room with Bob standing nearby and listening.

Gary (to Joe): This Doris Newman might be an easy target. And I like that.

Joe (skeptical): You still don't know how Doris Newman is going to take this.

Gary: Every bit of data in your file pans out. She's got the money in the bank to cover what I want for my documentary.

Joe: How much?

Gary: Two hundred grand.

Joe nods positively, admiring Gary's guts.

Kenny: And Mead doesn't get any of it.

Joe: But the target doesn't know that.

Kansas: And Mead gives away his share.

Gary (to Joe): Did he say who gets his share?

Joe: Not yet. I'll pin him down when it's done. How would you approach this target?

Gary: I thought I'd get her to meet me at a mall in an open area where I could show her this interview.

Joe (positive nod): Good. That's smart.

Gary: I thought I'd give her more time.

Joe: How much time?

Gary: She pays the day before Mead's parole board hearing.

Joe: And she testifies on Mead's behalf.

Gary: Right.

Joe: Sounds real good, Gary.

Kenny (to Joe): When is Mead's hearing?

Bob (whispers to Kenny): August thirteenth ... your lucky day.

Kenny: How's that my lucky day?

Joe: That's Donna's fight night, right?

Kenny: That's right.

Now Kenny feels he has to say something to Joe. Gary sees it coming and tries to stop Kenny from talking to his dad.

Kenny: Dad, I goofed up on something -

Gary: Kenny, maybe now isn't a good time.

Joe (to Kenny): What?

Kenny: I told Donna you could arrange for her dad to see her next fight.

Bob and Joe exchange knowing looks.

Joe: Why would you tell her that?

Kenny: To impress her, so she'd go out with me.

Joe: So she'd go out with you?

Kenny nods yes knowing he was selfish and stupid.

Joe: Was this her idea or yours?

Kenny: Mine.

Gary sees that Joe is really upset with Kenny and intervenes.

Gary: Joe, Kenny told me about this and I didn't get a chance to tell him what I came up with.

Joe and the crew listen to Gary's MUTED idea he'd come up with for Kenny.

*****

A few days later, in a Wichita mall common area, Gary is dressed for business seated at a small and private table with briefcase and open laptop on the table as DORIS NEWMAN, 55-60, Caucasian, enters the mall wearing sunglasses with baseball cap in casual attire. She does not want to be recognized. Doris walks over to Gary. Dialog is MUTED as Gary invites her to sit and watch the Mead interview with earbuds she inserts as:

SERIES OF SHOTS:

In the same MMA gym, we HEAR the song "Sunshine" by Atmosphere coming from Kenny's inserted earbud while working out in the gym. Kenny watches Donna spar with trainer Cory. The song continues through this series of shots.

Later, in same mall common area, Doris Newman appears shaken after watching interview with Gary and her former son-in-law. As

Gary packs up they have MUTED words when Gary hands Newman a manila envelope before he stands and leaves with his things. Newman opens the envelope and begins reading Gary's proposal until she gets her cell phone and speed-dials a number before her MUTED conversation on her cell phone. Now, some 50 feet away, Kansas has been discreetly filming and listening to Newman's phone conversation via hidden mic Gary planted under a table top.

That night, in the crew's rental house, Gary, Kansas, and Kenny watch and listen to Newman's MUTED phone call in the mall and high-five each other in celebration upon hearing Newman's incriminating words. The music fades out.

END SERIES OF SHOTS

*****

Outside the MMA gym, Donna walks to her car after a workout. Kenny stands behind his Mustang that's parked behind her car. He's dressed in his best clothes. She likes Kenny and stops to talk.

Kenny (contrite): I was wrong telling you I could get your dad to your next fight. (beat) But I still have a cool way he could at least see your fight the next day.

Donna: I just heard my fight was postponed.

Kenny: Really?

Donna: She supposedly sprained her hand sparring.

Kenny: Supposedly?

Donna (confident): She's afraid of me. She knows when I kick her ass in the first round she's out of the top twenty and I'm in. (beat) And, I don't have a manager. Fight promoters don't like dealing with fighters who don't have representation.

176

Kenny: Why don't you have a manager?

Donna: Kenny, good fights are good matchups. I don't want a good fight. I want to take her out in the first round. I'll keep winning and make my own deals.

Kenny (flirting): This might be perfect timing to relax and hang out with a distraction. Besides, you've got to at least hear about how your dad sees your next fight.

She's considering it, and intrigued.

*****

Later, at the crew's house, Kenny returns home after talking to Donna; he's excited to share the good news with Gary about Gary's plan to help Kenny get a date with Donna. Gary and Kansas are watching a movie on the big screen TV. Kenny sits near Gary and Kansas pauses the movie.

Kenny (to Gary): It worked. I'm going out with her tonight.

Gary: Great! I have good news, too.

Kenny: What's that?

Gary: I pitched the target today.

Kenny: Already?

Kansas (animated): We've got her on the phone with her daughter telling her that they have to pay Gary two hundred grand. She talked about moving her stolen jewelry out of state and how she has to testify on Mead's behalf at his parole hearing!

Kenny (to Kansas & Gary): So you don't have any work for me on this one?

Gary: Nope. You're free and clear to pursue Donna "The Bell" Snyder.

Kenny: I told her your idea that you told Joe and we're going out tonight.

Gary: Sweet.

Kenny: Just take out you know what and we're square. How much from this target?

Gary (smiles): Two hundred thousand. Can you believe it?

Kenny: So that's ... like fifty grand for me and Kansas to split?

Gary (looks at Kansas): Yeah. That deal you made is off. Buy me lunch some time.

Kenny (to Kansas): This Law of Attraction stuff you've been talking to me about since you came back from California?

Kansas (smiles): Yeah?

Kenny: It's working for me. (puts arm around Gary) Thanks to this man ... I'm going to be Donna's manager.

Kansas & Gary: What?

Kansas: Are you serious?

Kenny: That's the plan.

Gary: Did Donna say you could manage her?

Kenny: Not yet. She will.

Gary: What about our crew?

Kenny: I'll do both until I can't.

Kenny leaves the room to get ready for his date. Kansas resumes playing the movie, not wanting to get into it with Kenny right now about his plans to manage Donna.

Gary (watching movie): Can I watch my dad's interview tonight?

Kansas: Sure. It's ready. I sent it to you some time ago.

Gary dreads watching the interview he did with his dad in Yuma.

*****

Later that evening, outside the crew's house, Kenny exits the house dressed for his date with Donna. He gets into his Mustang, starts it and drives off as:

In Traveller, Gary watches Kenny drive away. Gary looks down to his open laptop on Traveller's table, turns off the lights and positions the laptop screen so he can watch his dad's interview from the couch.

On laptop screen: Kansas films Gary walking into his dad's cluttered Airstream; she uses a shoulder-mounted camera. Inside the Airstream, Arnie sits rocking slowly in his rocking chair, ready to push his son's buttons as the interview begins.

Arnie: This is that interview you've been talking about.

Gary: Yeah, Dad, I'll just sit close to you here.

Gary sits on his dad's messy sofa, clearing away stuff before positioning himself next to his dad for the camera.

Arnie: I know what this is really about.

Gary (frustrated): What are you talking about, Dad?

179

Arnie: It's about me calling you a hack all these years! You're a vanity writer for Christ's sake! You publish any self-indulgent tripe that suits you!

Arnie's laugh upsets Gary, though he tries to not show it, because Gary knows his dad is pushing his buttons.

Gary (on camera): I didn't come here to tell you how good I'm doing with my vanity writing, Dad. But then since you judge everything by money, because you saved your money your whole life so you could die in your Airstream because you're so damn stubborn! I get that, Dad!

Arnie: Get me a beer.

Gary gets his dad a cold beer from the fridge while Kansas moves to get another angle for when Gary sits back down next to his dad.

Arnie: And I know you're only doing this interview to get me committed to that V. A. Home you want to put me in! All they'll do is dry me out until I run off again!

Kansas (to Arnie off screen): You lived in the V. A. Home here?

Arnie (hard of hearing): What?

Gary (to Kansas): Yes, he's lived in the V. A. Home here. He agreed to try it out, see how he liked it. He didn't like it, so he left. He got his Airstream out of storage and he moved here.

Kansas (off screen): Gary, why do you think your father should go back to the V. A.?

Gary (counts on fingers): Let's see: Because he gets drunk on two beers. His brain is pickled. He falls asleep in his chair with a TV dinner in the oven. He smokes in bed! (rising anger) He shouldn't be driving at all! Or walking into a Dairy Queen in his

180

underwear! (softer) Hey look, it's a matter of time before he hurts himself or someone else. (to Arnie) You're too old to live alone, Dad. So yeah, I would show this to the V. A. You'd get dried out and live in a little cottage on the V. A. grounds, separated from the hospital. You just couldn't drive or leave the grounds on your own.

Arnie (gets out of chair): I want to show you something on the V. A. grounds, Mr. Vanity Writer. (gets walking cane) I think you'll change your tune.

Gary (to Kansas on camera): Okay. Let's go.

Kansas turns off her camera and they exit Arnie's Airstream.

*****

Later, on the expansive Yuma V. A. Hospital grounds, Kansas sits between the men in Arnie's old truck; she's taping with her hand-held camera as Arnie points to where he wants Gary to park in the shade of an old tree on an isolated part of the V. A. grounds. As the old man stares at the big tree:

Gary (to Arnie): Right here? You want me to park here, Dad?

Arnie gets out of his truck with the aid of his walking cane and walks toward the tree as Kansas gets out and follows Arnie on camera.

Gary (off screen): This is crazy! I'm paying a grand for this! Why are we here, Dad?

Kansas and Gary reach Arnie, who is counting his steps to himself to find a place on the ground, whereupon Arnie stops and starts digging into the ground with his cane.

Gary (off screen): Dad, what are you doing?

Arnie kneels down and after a bit more digging with his hands he removes a black plastic bag. Gary takes the bag and inside the bag is a handgun. Gary checks to see if the gun is loaded.

Arnie: It's not loaded.

Gary (puts gun back in bag): What's this all about, Dad?

Arnie starts walking with his cane back toward his truck with Kansas and Gary close behind.

Gary (harping): Dad, what is this? You buried a gun here!

Arnie (stops & turns to Gary): I buried two guns here. The other one's loaded. That's my way out if I can't live my life on my terms.

Now Gary understands his father's appeal. They have a moment. As Arnie continues back to his truck, Gary really thinks things over, now wanting to help his dad as Kansas continues filming. Kansas follows Gary to the truck.

Gary: Dad, I'm making more money now than I ever have in my whole life. I can afford to pay for some in-home professional care, someone to come into your place for physical therapy, whatever.

Arnie (reaches car & rests): How much does help like that cost?

Gary: Twenty-five bucks an hour for a professional. She could come by a few hours twice a week.

Kansas (off screen): And a weekly cleaning service!

Gary (to Arnie): And a weekly cleaning service. We can set it up now before we leave.

Arnie leans on his cane.

Arnie (smiles at Gary): You know I'm too tight to spend the money on myself like that.

Gary (laughs in agreement): I know, Dad. I'm the same way. (to Kansas) I'd laugh too if I was you, getting a grand to point a camera at us.

They climb into the old truck, all laughing. Kansas sits between them. Gary is behind the wheel as Kansas films them driving away.

Gary (off screen): On to the Arizona Department of Human Resources to find some good in-home care for my Dad!

Kansas (off screen): And a cleaning service!

Gary (off screen): I was going to say that … Karen!

Kansas turns her camera off.

*****

Back in Traveller, Gary smiles, closes his laptop, then writes out a check to Karen Long for one thousand dollars.

*****

Meanwhile, Kenny parks his Mustang near Donna's car in front of a cozy 1950's one-bedroom lakeside cottage. Kenny walks to the back of the house and onto a lakeside deck where he hears the song "Sunshine" by Atmosphere coming from inside the cottage. The music is loud and he knocks on the back patio glass sliding door.

Donna (off screen): Come in!

Kenny steps inside and is surprised at the early-1970's look of the cottage: black lights and 1970-era posters, floor pillows, and fishnets hang from the low ceiling. The music stops and Donna enters the front room through beads hanging from a bedroom entrance. To Kenny, she is beautiful in casual jeans and T-shirt.

183

Kenny: I love this early-seventies look.

Donna: Summer of seventy-two to be exact. My dad was sixteen when his grandpa left him this place in his will.

Kenny: Really? Nice crib.

Donna: My dad said I could live here when I turned eighteen. I found all his stuff packed here and one day I just put things up here and there until it was like he had it.

Kenny follows her into the small kitchen.

Kenny: Could you get me a Press Pass for your next fight? I want to shoot it.

Donna doesn't answer him; she dishes rice and beans onto plates from the stove and they eat at a table for two in the tiny kitchen. She opens the fridge:

Donna: All I have is bottled water to drink.

Kenny: That's fine.

She hands Kenny a bottle of water and sits down to eat with him.

Donna: I just got a fight.

Kenny (eating): Really? Where?

Donna: Here, a week from next Saturday.

Kenny: Wow. That's short notice. Who?

Donna (eating): Cory says she's an undefeated unknown like me. I said I'd take it.

Kenny: Donna, I'd really like to manage you and be your agent.

Donna: Is that why you want to shoot my fight, to promote me?

184

Kenny (frankly): No. But that's a good idea. (beat) My dad could show your fight to your dad the next day. I know my dad would do that if I sent your fight to my dad's laptop. (beat) Again, I'm really sorry I got your hopes up earlier about your dad coming to your fight. That was my ego.

Donna: What are your terms to represent me?

Kenny: Twenty percent of everything you make related to fighting.

Donna: What about expenses?

Kenny: I cover all my expenses.

Donna: No fees or hidden costs?

Kenny: That's right. I'll draw up a contract. (beat) Does Cory arrange your fights?

While eating, Donna nods yes.

Kenny: What do you pay him?

Donna: Fifteen per cent of my purse.

Kenny thinks about that while he eats.

Kenny: Does he charge you to train at his gym?

Donna: Not now. I let him use my name to promote the gym.

Kenny nods positively.

Kenny: You do know that if you keep winning you'll have to change trainers and move to a world class gym where the top-ranked fighters train?

Donna (smiles): We'll see.

Kenny: What's your goal?

Donna: To get a UFC contract and win the belt.

Kenny (pressing): Why?

Donna (intensely): I have to be something other than the girl whose father killed her mother.

Kenny gives his understanding nod.

Kenny: I know what you mean. And I like your motivation. It's real and powerful like your stand-up.

Donna likes the idea of Kenny managing her.

Kenny: I can have a contract for you to sign before your fight.

Donna (smiles): Okay.

Kenny: Really?

Donna gives a positive nod as they enjoy their meal and MUTED conversation and laughter as "Bad Case of Loving You" sung by Robert Palmer plays throughout:

SERIES OF SHOTS:

In a Wichita parole board hearing room, target Doris Newman testifies to PAROLE BOARD to release her former son-in-law, inmate Glen Mead.

In same mall common area, target Doris Newman drops off an envelope to Gary, now seated at the same table of their first meeting. Doris keeps walking. Gary opens the envelope and smiles at the cashier's check made out to him for $200,000.00.

Daytime in Arnie's Yuma RV park, in Arnie's Airstream, happy Arnie does physical therapy exercises with his new female

PHYSICAL THERAPIST as his new CLEANING SERVICE WOMAN cleans the interior of his Airstream.

As the song plays in Wichita sports arena, Donna knocks out BANTAMWEIGHT OPPONENT early in the first round as Kenny tapes the fight discreetly with a digital camera while seated on the same reserved seat for Donna's father.

Later, Cory and Kenny wait for Donna after her fight. She exits the locker room after showering. Her new agent/manager and trainer embrace her together in celebration.

Next day, in Mead's prison cell, Mead discreetly gives Bob a folded piece of paper that Bob puts inside his shirt pocket without reading while walking away from Mead's cell.

A bit later, Joe's working on his laptop at his writing table when Bob walks over and hands him Mead's folded note from his shirt pocket. Joe opens the folded paper and reads the note before giving the note to Bob for him to read, whereupon they both appear surprised by the note we do not see as Robert Palmer fades out.

END SERIES OF SHOTS

NEXT DAY

On Bingham's parking lot, we see Kenny's parked Mustang.

In common visiting area, inmate JIMMY SNYDER, 50, Caucasian punch-drunk fighter, watches his daughter's MUTED fight on Joe's laptop. Jimmy is seated next to Joe at a table at the back of the room with Donna seated across from her father. Kenny is seated across from Joe with uniformed Bob standing within earshot. When Joe closes his laptop after Donna's first-round knockout, Jimmy starts to cry, covering his face with his hands. Joe motions for Kenny to get up from the table with him to give Jimmy and Donna privacy; they soon stand near Bob as Donna reaches for and places

187

her father's hands on the table with her hands on top of his as they talk softly.

Donna (compassionate): What's wrong, Dad?

Jimmy Snyder (slow & deliberate): When I hit your mother … I wanted to kill her. That's what my punch-drunk brain told me. I don't want that kind of life for you.

Donna rolls her eyes, having heard this before.

Jimmy Snyder: Listen to me, little girl. Moving up the ranks you'll face better and better fighters who will hit you.

Donna: Dad, this is MMA. I'm a female Lyoto Machida. I don't let them hit me.

Jimmy Snyder: Maybe not now … but they will. It happened to me. I got jabbed a hell of a lot more than I got my bell rung.

Donna (discreet pleading): Dad, I signed a contract with Kenny to manage me. I've got a chance to move up faster now.

Jimmy Snyder: Listen to me, baby girl. You still have your passport?

Donna: Yeah, why?

Jimmy Snyder: I'm selling the cottage. I want you to take the money and explore Europe like you wanted to do before I came here.

Donna's shocked and warming up to the idea as Jimmy leans forward.

Jimmy Snyder: I know the fighter's life, Donna. It's part of why I'm in here. I know what I did screwed up my life and damaged yours terribly. (tearful) Please stay away from fighting. You're all I got left.

Donna cries with her eyes closed, still holding her father's hands and nodding positively that she will do what her father wants, to Kenny's chagrin.

*****

A few days later, at Donna's lakeside cottage, Kenny parks his Mustang near a loaded U-Haul truck. He gets out of his car as Donna exits the cottage carrying a few items. He was upset about their broken contract, and has let it go. They stand face-to-face and talk.

Kenny (contrite): Sorry I didn't help you load your stuff. I was thinking about me and not you, so … I'm sorry. (upset) But I can't believe you sold this place so fast.

Donna puts down her things and they hold each other as they talk.

Kenny (eyes closed): I quit the gym, too.

She laughs, still embracing each other in this playful MMA clinch against the cage, a grappling dance with their eyes closed. She moves Kenny in a dominant way. He's too scared to open his eyes, to experience intimacy, because he never has before.

Donna (sensual tease): I wanted us to work out here, on the back deck to my music.

Kenny (turned on): Yeah?

Donna (confronts him): Not really. (she explains) Because you're not here.

Kenny (opens eyes): What do you mean?

Donna (smiles): There you are. (beat) I mean, I would never become intimate with my manager.

Kenny understands as they stand face-to-face connected.

Kenny: I was thinking how someday you'll see that your dad's right about this.

Donna: I already do. And I am doing what's right for me.

Kenny almost forgot to give her the envelope in his pocket.

Donna: What's this?

Kenny: A cashier's check for fifty grand. That's what your dad sold this place for. My dad told me to give it to you. This is your chance to explore Europe.

Donna is tearfully happy when she sees her money.

Donna: Now it's real. And now I can travel like I always wanted.

Again she hugs Kenny. Just then, Traveller drives up and parks near her rental truck. Gary carries personal items with him when he gets out from behind the wheel. Gary walks over to them.

Gary: Hi, Donna. I'm Gary. Can I move my stuff in?

Donna: Sure, Gary. The keys to the front and back doors are on the table in the kitchen.

Kenny (to Gary): You bought this place?

Gary smiles and walks toward his new home.

Kenny (to Donna): I don't get it. Gary's too cheap to buy this place or any place.

*****

A few days later, at the Wichita airport, Kenny watches Donna's flight take off via the observation window. Then he walks away.

Inside the airport parking garage, Kenny gets into his Mustang and exits the parking garage as Bob discreetly observes Kenny driving out of parking garage and emails a message on his cell phone. We do not see the message … yet.

*****

Joe, seated at his desk in his private prison cell, sees his brief email message from Bob on his laptop screen: "she's gone."

We do not see who Joe forwards the same message to:

Inside the crew's rental house, Kansas reads the same forwarded message from Joe: "she's gone." Kansas is relieved to get this message.

End of Episode 4

Episode 5:

Gary's Home

Summer is ending and fall is in the air this evening as Kansas drives Kenny to Gary's new home, the same lakeside cottage Donna Snyder's father sold a couple weeks ago. Inside the moving red Jeep:

Kansas: I found out on our trip to Yuma that Gary's never owned his own house before, except for Traveller.

Kenny: So this is a big deal for him.

Kansas: Yeah … but maybe not.

Kenny: So what's your point?

Kansas: I don't have a point.

Kenny: I think Gary bought this place for Joe, and Gary's living there rent-free until Joe gets out. Turn here.

Kansas parks the Jeep near Traveller in front of the lakeside cottage.

Kansas: This place is nice. He can park Traveller right here. It's the perfect size for him. Kenny, you should've met Gary's dad. Did you ever see his interview with his dad?

Kenny: No.

Kansas: Watch it sometime and you'll see why Gary is -

Kenny: Gary?

Kansas: Yeah.

They laugh getting out of the Jeep while walking to the open front door. They knock on the front door, announce their arrival and enter the cottage after no answer.

Kenny (calling out): Gary's home!

They stand in the front room looking at the comfortable furnishings now in the cottage: a modest dining table for 4 with 3 place settings in the dining room area of the front room with a recliner facing a flat screen TV with swivel reading light on a table next to the recliner where they see Gary's writing folder, road atlas, and a coffee cup holding pens and pencils with his black bag hanging on the open bedroom doorknob. Kenny goes into the bedroom and Kansas goes into the kitchen and looks out the kitchen window. Kansas sees Gary sitting on the dock in a chair with his back to the house facing the lake. Kansas is the first to reach Gary on the dock.

Kansas: He invites us to his new crib and there's nothing! No food, no Gary -

Gary wipes his eyes and when Kenny arrives, Gary turns to Kansas and she sees that Gary has been crying.

Kansas (concerned): What's wrong?

Gary (embarrassed): Oh, nothing.

Kansas puts her arm around Gary.

Gary: I guess I've been feeling sorry for myself. I'm so pathetic. (laughs) Living here in my first home... I've been alone with my thoughts ... uh ... seeing how I could end up alone like my dad. It's like I've set up my life to end up this way ... alone.

193

Thompson Sawyer Library
403 W. 3rd
Quanah, Texas 79252
940-663-2654

9/27/2017 @ 11:13am

Roberts, Kenneth
2TSPL0C002469/

Today's Check Outs

Already Bad Vol 1-Episodes 1-5
Barcode: 3TSPL0003382G8
Due Date: 10/11/2017

Driving heat
Barcode: T 24763
Due Date: 10/11/2017

Kansas (consoling): That won't happen. We're your family now. And hey, now you have a great place to entertain a woman.

Kenny: Yeah, this is a cool crib, Gary. I wish Donna still lived here.

Gary chuckles.

Kansas: Now you have the perfect chance to create the kind of space and people you want in your life. You lived in Traveller to learn how to live alone. Now you can start manifesting your new life with new relationships.

Gary nods in agreement. As they walk toward the cottage:

Kenny: What's for dinner, Gary? I'm starved.

Gary: I thought I'd order pizza or Chinese.

Kenny: Sweet.

*****

Later that evening, having pizza at Gary's new table, Kansas has left all her thin pizza crust on her plate, eating very little of the toppings.

Gary: You don't like the pizza?

Kansas: I'm gluten-intolerant.

Gary: What's that mean?

Kansas: I went to a naturopath and found out my body can't handle gluten. And about everything has gluten in it. Millions of people are eating gluten-free and feeling better.

Gary: How do you know if you're gluten-intolerant?

Kansas: I feel better when I don't put gluten in my body.

194

Gary: What are some of the symptoms if you're gluten-intolerant?

Kansas: Constipation, low energy, mood swings.

Kenny: No kidding.

Gary: Where is this naturopath?

*****

The next day, Kansas and Gary leave the naturopath's office and walk to the Jeep.

Gary: I'm gluten intolerant. All these years and now I find out.

Kansas: Don't beat yourself up. Your body gradually came to this point after a poor diet for decades. You were meant to find out now.

Gary (getting into Jeep): Another universal law?

Kansas: If you eat shit … shit happens.

Gary laughs.

*****

It's another Indian summer day in Kansas, as Bob, wearing casual clothes, parks his truck near Traveller in front of Gary's cottage. On the cottage front door is a note for Bob.

Bob (reads note): Gone fishing.

Bob walks around to the lake side of the cottage and sees Gary reading on a lawn chair on the dock. Gary's wearing sunglasses and a baseball cap. There's a fishing pole with a line in the water and there's a tackle box nearby. Bob enters the back door of the cottage and comes back outside with a beer in hand. Gary hears Bob open his beer behind him.

Bob: Some life you got, Gary! Catch anything?

Gary sits up on the lawn chair, straddling it with his feet on the dock; he's happy to see Bob.

Gary: Nothing yet.

Bob: Early morning or early evening is the best time to catch bullheads.

Gary: You've fished here?

Bob (fondly): Many times. Joe and I used to skip school and come here. We wouldn't fish. We'd bum smokes from fishermen and hang out with 'em. Sometimes they'd give us a beer or a pop. We weren't fussy.

They laugh.

Gary: When Joe asked me if I'd live in this house if he bought it from Snyder, I thought, 'Yeah,'; and then when he said I'd just have to pay the taxes, utilities, and keep up the place. I said, 'I'm in.'

Bob: You know why Joe bought this place?

Gary: He said he couldn't take the share Mead gave him, so he gave his share to Snyder for the deed to this place. That was how Snyder could give fifty grand to his daughter to go to Europe.

Bob kneels down to Gary's eye level:

Bob: Gary … Joe did that to keep you here until he gets out.

Gary: Joe expects me to live here for eight years?

Bob shakes his head no.

Bob: He doesn't expect anything. He knows you're doing a great job managing his crew.

Gary: Joe said that?

Bob: Many times he's told me how he got lucky with you as his crew manager. Gary, this is how Joe keeps his kids in his life.

Gary understands.

Bob: How far do you think the cases Joe found would go if Karen and Kenny pitched the targets?

Another understanding nod from Gary.

Gary: This thing that Joe does behind prison walls is going to change the penal system in many ways and I believe bring our crime rate down.

Bob: It already has.

Gary: I know that you and Joe go way back as foster brothers, but could I ask you something without offending you?

Bob: Sure. What?

Gary (into Bob's eyes): Buying this place from Jimmy Snyder, did Joe see that as a way to get Donna out of Kenny's life?

Bob: I honestly couldn't say one way or the other if that was part of his reasoning.

Gary: Okay. Fair enough. I just wonder if Kenny has thought of that.

Bob: You could ask Joe. But I know Joe, and his intentions are pure. He loves his kids.

Gary nods positively in agreement, adding:

Gary: I was just curious. I know Kenny was planning on managing Donna's career and that might clash with our thing.

Bob (confiding tone): To tell you the truth, Jimmy Snyder did not want his daughter to be a fighter. Her last fight really got to Jimmy. When Jimmy got his share and gave it to Joe, they made the deal for this place so Jimmy could get her out of the fight game.

Understanding nod from Gary. Just then: Gary's fishing line has a serious bite.

Bob: You got one!

Gary grabs his fishing pole, stands and reels in a small bullhead, which he unhooks and throws back into the lake, causing Bob to laugh.

*****

NEXT DAY

Joe sits across from Warden Ted in the warden's office with a file in hand; they are discussing three inmates to be released early if Joe has no objections.

Joe (refers to file): This William Simpson: he's good. He's been educating himself. He's turned himself into a voracious reader. He's about as rehabilitated as anyone I've ever interviewed.

Warden Ted (making notes): Okay. Simpson is good. What about … (looks at file) Clevis Williams?

Joe: Yes, Clevis. I interviewed him just last week and he's good to go. He's got no axe to grind with anyone or society as far as I can tell. He found Jesus not long after he arrived here. I'd bet on him doing well when he gets out.

Warden Ted (reading file): Yes, I agree.

Joe (consternation): And finally, Jesse Lee Clay. Manslaughter, three years served.

Warden Ted: He's the guy who was mad at his girlfriend and took a hammer to her car.

Joe (nodding yes): Right. The hammer flew out of his hand and hit and killed a man on his patio who'd been watching the whole scene with his wife. Freak accident for Clay and (checks file) George Townsend. Hit him right between his eyes. Killed him instantly. Townsend's wife, Michele, was a witness and testified that Clay was in a drunken rage.

Warden Ted: Anger. That's the killer. As we all know about anger -

Joe (finishes warden's words): One letter away from danger.

Warden Ted: Exactly.

Joe: Warden, I think I should interview this Jesse Clay. This was a young man with no criminal record who killed a man by accident. I interviewed him when he'd only been in here a few months.

Warden Ted: I agree. Better safe than sorry. He could be mad at the world after a thousand days and nights locked up for some stupid, drunken accident.

Joe: I'd like my crew to film my interview with Clay.

Warden Ted: Karen and Kenny?

Joe: And Mr. Fleming. And, uh, Warden Ted, Karen wants to be called Kansas now.

Warden Ted: Kansas?

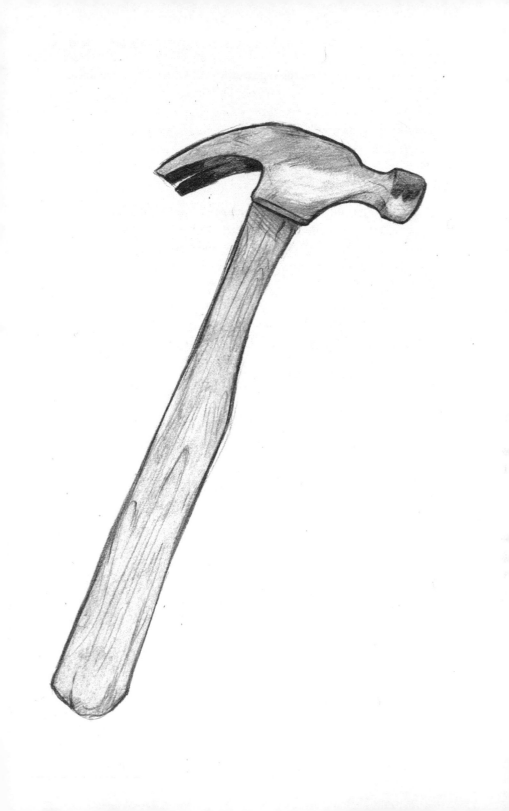

Joe: It's a long story. (changes subject) I know The Corporation is looking for ways to make money. This Jesse Clay interview: I want my crew to follow the source of the anger in Clay. Maybe there's a short documentary there Mr. Fleming could market ... if you agree, sir.

Warden Ted (sits back in chair): Interesting.

Joe: Let me add, Warden, Bingham is a big holding facility for overcrowded state facilities. Your staff is supposed to evaluate and place these inmates in maximum or minimum security prisons here or in other facilities. I believe with my crew we can establish a proven alternative for state or corporate-owned prisons to send us their inmates due for early release and upcoming time-served parolees for evaluation. I believe we can lower the rate of recidivism in other facilities as we have in Bingham.

Warden Ted is thinking it over.

Warden Ted: Joe, if you can interview Clay and make this documentary without you leaving Bingham, I'm willing to give it a try. I don't want one of my inmates seen in a documentary off prison grounds.

The warden gets up from behind his desk and Joe stands up with his files in hand.

Warden Ted: If you come up with a compelling documentary ... I can present it to Denver and see where it leads.

Joe: Karen ... Kansas has been putting together charts and graphs from information I've given her that you could present to The Board along with an interesting documentary.

Warden Ted: I'll see what I can do.

They shake hands and Joe exits the warden's office.

*****

Later, in the Bingham dining hall, Joe sits across the table from Officer Bob; they're having lunch together. Joe is excited about his recent meeting with Warden Ted.

Bob: I can't believe The Corporation is going to let you film a documentary for Gary to market.

Joe: The Board has to approve it. But this is such an opportunity because Gary can use our crew to film and market stories from my files. No more targets.

Bob: You mean blackmail.

Joe (smiles): Only the targets call it blackmail.

Bob: I don't know about marketing documentaries. Gary likes making money. I got the feeling he knows he's not getting any younger and the targets have made him some easy money. He's got a hard road behind him. When I was out at the cottage he told me about all the places he's lived but never really had a home until now. That cat's been all over the country.

Joe: I know. I've read all his books.

Bob: How many books has he written?

Joe: I don't know, maybe thirty.

Bob: And you've read every one?

Joe nods yes.

Bob: Is he a good writer?

Another positive nod, adding:

Joe: That's why I picked him to manage our crew.

Bob: Where can I get one of his books?

Joe: Go to your library. They can get titles for you.

Bob: I'll do that. Which one should I read first?

Joe removes a notebook pad from his shirt pocket, and with his pen he writes down a title and pushes it across the table to Bob.

Bob (reads note): Ledges. I think Kansas said she read that and couldn't put it down.

Joe: Make sure you get the 2005 edition with the red cover. It's the third printing with a new ending. Read that one first. Gary told me he wrote the script to Ledges and could see Chris Cooper playing his character, Dutch, with Matthew McConaughey playing Gene, the bus driver.

Bob removes a pen from his shirt pocket and writes on the same note:

Bob (mumbles): 2005…third printing.

*****

That night, Gary watches a baseball game on his flat screen TV from his recliner in the cottage when he sees that he has a message from Kansas on his laptop screen that he swivels over to his lap to read on the screen: *Gary, open the file from Joe. Interview tomorrow at noon at Bingham. Kenny and I will see you there. Exciting. Love you, Kansas.*

Gary opens the file on Jesse Lee Clay, 32, Caucasian. We see Clay's Bingham headshot in blue jumpsuit and read Joe's notes: *Jesse Clay was sentenced to serve 6 years for involuntary manslaughter ...*

{FLASHBACK}:

Outside a Wichita apartment complex in 2012, JESSE CLAY is a drunk driver and enraged when he parks his car and gets a hammer from his trunk as MICHELE & GEORGE TOWNSEND, 30-something, stand nearby on their ground-level apartment patio having a smoke when they see Clay smashing and breaking windows on his girlfriend's car until the hammer flies out of his hand, striking George Townsend between his eyes, killing him instantly. His stunned wife, Michele, is on her cell phone calling 911.

{END OF FLASHBACK}

We HEAR Joe's message that Gary reads on his laptop:

Joe (voice over): *Gary, what we want to find out is if there's an interesting documentary here that you can market to and for The Corporation. Clay's release date is approaching and we must know if his anger issue is alive toward his ex-girlfriend.*

Gary now reads with intense interest Joe's file on laptop screen that Kansas forwarded to him.

*****

In Kansas and Kenny's rental house, Kansas is practicing yoga on the floor in the front room when she stops, goes into the hallway and knocks on Kenny's closed bedroom door.

Kenny (off screen): Enter!

Kenny is playing a video game while lying on his bed and continues playing the game while talking to his sister.

Kenny: What's up?

Kansas: We've got an interview with Joe tomorrow at noon.

Kenny: Sweet.

203

Kansas: Could you pause that for a minute, please?

Kenny pauses his game and Kansas stands over him.

Kansas: Have you noticed Gary's acting strange lately?

Kenny: No stranger than the usual strange.

Kansas: I went over to the cottage yesterday and he didn't answer the door. I could hear his Chris Rea music was on and Traveller was there.

Kenny: Maybe he went for a walk.

Kansas: No. I heard the volume turned down after I knocked.

Kenny: Maybe he was gettin' busy.

Kansas laughs, then her brother laughs too.

*****

Later that night, Gary is going to bed in his cottage when he sees headlights on outside his front window. He looks out from behind his front room blinds and sees a cab parked near Traveller. He sees MELISSA, 44, Caucasian, get out of the cab as the cab driver removes a suitcase out of his trunk and drives away. This somewhat attractive woman wheels her suitcase to Traveller's back door, unlocks the door with a key and goes inside with her suitcase. Gary sees a light come on inside his RV. Now Gary questions his generosity, letting this woman he met in a bar and brought home last night, stay in Traveller until she can get her own place "in a few days."

Gary (to himself): How lonely and pathetic can I get … to have a one-night stand and let a relative stranger stay in Traveller a few days. What was I thinking? I'm too old for this.

*****

NEXT DAY

Gary, dressed for work, comes out of his cottage carrying a cup of coffee for his guest. He knocks on Traveller's back door. No answer. He knocks louder. Still no answer. Gary decides to unlock his door with his key.

Gary: Melissa? It's Gary!

Still no response from his guest. Gary steps up into his RV and sees that Melissa's body is covered by a blanket on his couch.

Gary: Melissa? Got fresh coffee here! Wake up, please! I have an appointment and I can't be late!

Still no movement. Gary shakes her shoulder and then sees an empty prescription bottle on the floor next to the couch. He turns on the light to read the prescription bottle and reads:

Gary: Valium.

Gary checks her pulse and gets a faint pulse. He quickly gets behind the wheel and speed-dials Kansas. He drives away fast.

Gary (on cell phone): I got a situation here. I need the nearest hospital to the cottage and fast.

Kansas, getting ready for the interview at Bingham, hurries to her laptop and searches for the nearest hospital.

Kansas (on cell phone): What happened?

Gary drives Traveller faster than he ever has.

Gary (on cell phone): Can't explain now.

Kansas (on cell phone): Get on 135 South. Third exit is Marvin Avenue. Turn right there. Maybe five minutes away.

Gary (on cell phone): Can you pick me up there? I'm almost out of gas and I don't know how long I'll be. I can't be late for this interview.

Kansas (on cell phone): I'll meet you at the E. R. entrance.

Gary (on cell phone): Thanks, Kansas.

Gary speeds to hospital while flashing back to when he met Melissa:

{GARY'S FLASHBACK}:

Three nights ago, Traveller is parked in a bar's parking lot when Gary and Melissa exit the bar laughing and intoxicated as they near the front of Traveller.

Melissa: Where do you live?

Gary: Right here. This is my home.

They stop walking. Melissa laughs.

Melissa: You live here?

Gary: For twelve years.

Melissa is reluctant about going inside the RV.

Gary: I have another place, a cottage on Shawnee Lake.

Melissa: Let's go see your cottage.

Gary: I can't drive now. We can hang out here a few hours, have a bite to eat, listen to some music.

Melissa: I'm starved.

Gary kisses her and they go inside Traveller.

{END OF GARY'S FLASHBACK}

Gary parks Traveller in front of the hospital emergency room entrance and runs inside.

*****

A bit later, Melissa is carted away by hospital staff. Gary hands the admitting nurse Melissa's purse, suitcase, and empty prescription bottle.

Gary (to nurse): I don't know this person. Like I said, I found her outside on the sidewalk and brought her in here. I found her purse and this prescription bottle beside her.

Admitting Nurse (skeptical): On the sidewalk?

Gary: Yes! Everything was on the sidewalk ... the purse and the prescription bottle. End of story. And I have to go now.

Gary walks away from the admitting area, hoping this is the end of his involvement with Melissa. When Gary exits the hospital, Kansas is parked near Traveller with Kenny riding on the front passenger seat. Gary gets his black bag out of Traveller and gets into the Jeep's back seat.

*****

Later, in a Bingham private room, Bob stands guard as Joe interviews inmate Jesse Clay at a table with Kenny and Kansas behind cameras. Gary takes notes while seated in a corner.

Joe: Jesse, what made you so angry that you'd take a hammer to your girlfriend's car?

Jesse Clay: She was doing some guy that lived in the apartments there.

Joe: How do you know she was doing some guy?

Jesse Clay: The guy lives there. She was there.

Joe nods that he understands and looks at his notes.

Joe: How do you feel about your ex-girlfriend, Tory?

Jesse Clay: I don't feel anything.

Joe: Are you still angry at her? I mean, it's possible you might feel she's the reason you spent three years in Bingham.

Jesse Clay: I'm not angry about anything. At first I was. Then I was mad at myself for the whole scene. It's over with us. I mean, she didn't visit me once in here.

Joe: Was it a longtime or close relationship you had with Tory?

Jesse Clay: No ring or anything. I thought we were an item. (shrugs) No love lost.

Joe looks into Clay's eyes, trying to determine whether he is telling the truth, thus gaging whether Clay is a threat to his ex-girlfriend.

Joe: Has anyone contacted or visited you since you've been incarcerated in Bingham?

Jesse Clay: Just my family.

Joe: Any letters, phone calls, from anyone besides your family?

A negative nod from Clay. Joe looks over Clay's file.

Joe: Jesse, your visitation records say you have not had one visitor since arriving here. Why is that?

Kansas gets a close-up shot of Clay's aversion to Joe's line of questioning.

Jesse Clay: I don't know what you're getting at.

Joe: You said your family visited you here. Records show zero visitors. Not one visitor in three years, Jesse.

Jesse Clay (defensive): So?

Joe: So when you get out of here, I don't want you coming back. What I do is consult the warden whether or not you are a risk to hurting anyone after you're released.

Jesse Clay: My time is served. You can't hold me here 'cause I don't have any visitors. Sure I'm angry and I sure as hell don't want to come back here. You might be angry too if you were in here for three years for destroying property and you killed a guy by accident ... and ... (faltering) Nobody knows how sorry I am for killin' that guy over a woman I had no business bein' involved with. I always knew that my anger would do me in one day. (contrite) I got to thinkin' about how me and George Townsend had been on this planet maybe some sixty years combined and because of my stupid primal anger he's dead and I'm in here.

Jesse Clay: What do you want to do with your life when you get out of here, Jesse?

Jesse Clay (after deep breath): Part of me wants to start a new life somewhere where nobody knows me. Another part of me wants to do something for George Townsend's family. But then I think his family would not want me around to remind them of what I did.

Joe (reads file): I see in your file how you've had quite a bit of counselling regarding your anger issues since incarcerated. What have you learned in your sessions?

Jesse Clay: Yeah, I've come a long way. I learned that anger comes from fear, the opposite of love. It's much harder for me to show love than my negative patterns. I have to catch my negative thoughts, but they're so fast and automatic...it's hard.

Joe: Jesse, is there anything you'd say to your ex-girlfriend, Tory, if you could?

Jesse Clay (shaking head no): I got nothin' to say to her.

Joe: How about George Townsend's family, the man you accidently killed; is there anything you'd like to say to them?

Jesse Clay (contrite): I just uh … know I really hurt people I never meant to. I really am sorry. The best thing I can say to them is I will live a better life because of the awful thing I did. Sometimes I think I'll live a solitary life and nobody will ever know what I did. But I'm afraid I'll fall into a lonely, wasted life if I do that.

Joe (reading from file): During our last interview you said, "Before I came here I was unemployed for too long, getting high with my girlfriend with no plans to change my life." (puts file down) Jesse, in here you've had nothing but time to plan the changes you want when you leave Bingham. Give me something specific you plan to do with your life.

Jesse Clay: I thought I'd go west to Grand Junction. There's an ex-con there who hires drivers for his produce company.

Joe: Sounds good. (to Kansas & Kenny) That's good!

Joe stands and shakes hands with Jesse, then Bob comes over and escorts Jesse out of the room.

Joe (to crew): Meeting outside.

*****

A bit later, Joe finishes his smoke while writing notes in Jesse Clay's file at his private table when Bob escorts crew without their equipment over to the table. Bob has the crew sit across from Joe at the table.

Bob (joking to crew): Keep your hands on the table.

Joe (to Bob): What about me?

Bob: You can play with your pencil for all I care.

The crew laughs. Joe butts his smoke and tosses it into a butt can and opens Clay's file.

Joe: Okay. There's Jesse Lee Clay. Where do we go from here from what we know?

Kansas: We interview Jesse's ex-girlfriend and the victim's widow.

Gary: Jesse's right: No matter what we find out in the interviews - he still walks out of here when his time is served.

Joe (nods in agreement): He gets out in eleven days. (to Kenny) Get release forms signed. You're the front man. Nothing happens until you get things started. Do what it takes. But keep it legal.

Kansas: Everything we find out can help Jesse get a good start when he's released.

Gary: Jesse's risk potential to harm anyone when he gets out has to be a priority. The Corporation doesn't want him coming back to Bingham.

Joe: Exactly. I want this crew to help show inmates like Jesse Clay what's ahead of them when they get out. Ex-cons have a tough time getting good work when they're released. That's a real hurdle to rehabilitation and can lead to relapses.

Kansas: And that's not good for anybody.

Joe: That's right.

Gary: Who pays us for our work now?

Joe: If it's good, compelling enough …The Corporation will fund our documentaries. That's the plan anyway.

Gary: So no more targets?

Joe: I hope not. Let's see what Warden Ted can pitch to the board of directors in Denver.

Kansas: This sounds better. The targets felt like blackmail to me.

Gary: I liked the money.

Joe: I want us to move away from the target cases and create something good that helps the world be a better place. Something The Corporation will pay us for. We must find a way to help motivate inmates leaving prison to live well when they get out instead of repeating the same insanity that leads back here. Only the inmates who want to change are the ones we have a chance to live well when they get out.

Kenny: Like Jesse Clay?

Joe: Right. The incorrigibles and monsters in here that have no business getting out … I'll do my best to see that they stay here. Let's see if we can help inmates like Jesse Clay see what they're up against.

The crew is in agreement, seeing a good cause for making this documentary.

Joe: Kenny, I want you to step up your game getting these release forms. These are the victims of Clay. Some will not want anything to do with being interviewed. Only the ones with signed release forms are on camera. (beat) Kenny, you have to sell them on it or we have nothing. Understand?

Kenny: Yes, sir.

212

Kenny realizes this is the life philosophy Gary has been preaching to him: *We're all selling something, and will continue to sell, no matter who we are.*

Joe (to crew): Any questions?

Kansas: So we're going to interview these people who have something to say about Jesse. Then Jesse can see for himself where these people stand. If that's our goal then I think this is a positive tool for any inmate about to be released.

Everyone agrees.

Gary (asking for Kenny): What if any of these people want to be paid to be interviewed?

Joe: Good question. Nobody gets paid for an interview ... unless you want to pay them yourself.

Kenny (to Gary): That's already stated on a release form.

Joe (to Kenny): Good answer.

Kansas: I just want to say that this is one great opportunity for us to do some creative work without a hidden mic and a target to blackmail.

Gary (to Kansas): Our targets have been justified blackmail ... if there is such a thing.

Kenny (looks at file): Where do we start?

*****

Later, after Kansas drops Gary off at his parked RV outside the hospital emergency room, Gary gets behind the wheel of Traveller; but then Gary decides to go back inside the hospital.

213

Gary peeks into a hospital room and sees Melissa sleeping. Gary leaves.

*****

NEXT DAY

Kenny parks his Mustang in front of Michele's Dog Grooming business in Wichita. As Kenny walks toward the front entrance in his best clothes:

Joe (voice over): *George Townsend's widow, Michele, has a dog grooming business. She was standing beside her husband on their apartment patio watching Jesse Clay going crazy with a hammer on his girlfriend's car. She was the only witness and Kenny has to be wary and respectful when approaching her about this.*

Kenny enters the small dog grooming business with a release form in hand as financially struggling Michele Townsend greets Kenny from behind her counter. They are alone except for barking dogs in the back area of the shop as country music plays on a radio.

Kenny: Michele?

Michele: Yes.

Kenny: My name is Kenny Long. I represent independent documentary writer G. K. Fleming. He's doing a documentary on Jesse Clay's upcoming release from prison. Mr. Fleming asked me to stop by to see if you are willing to be interviewed in his documentary.

Michele (angry): Why would I do that? And what's in it for me?

Awkward pause.

Kenny: I'm not sure what you mean.

214

Michele: Do I get paid for this interview?

Kenny: No.

Michele: Then go away.

Kenny is caught off guard and leaves her shop. Walking back to his car:

Michele: Just a second!

Kenny is wary as the widow walks toward him. She stands a few feet from Kenny with her arms folded across her chest.

Michele: Why would anyone want to make a documentary about Jesse Clay?

Kenny: Mr. Fleming says it's all about rehabilitation and healing.

Michele (emotional): My husband and I started this business together. We opened this place a few months before that crazy bastard killed my husband.

Kenny understands, and Michele isn't finished.

Michele: My husband worked eighty hours a week so we could get this business going. I couldn't sue Clay because he doesn't have any money. There ought to be something Clay has to pay me when he gets out. Where's the justice for me?

Kenny: You could say all this in the documentary. Anything you want to say to Clay, Mr. Fleming will make sure Clay hears it. All you have to do is sign this release form.

Michele eyes the form in Kenny's hand and shakes her head no, getting in Kenny's face.

Michele: Clay took my husband, my business partner, my life. He did half the work around here. I don't know from one month to the next if I can stay open.

Kenny: Michele, Mr. Fleming makes documentaries that are real and need to be seen by some people. Because I'm part of his crew I can say that if you are in his documentary and he sells it … he's known to be generous to people who need help.

Kenny's words have given the financially struggling widow pause for thought.

Kenny (emotional): I know what you're going through. My dad is in prison because he caused the death of my mother. My sister and I had to forgive him in order to live our lives. My sister would spend time every day with me talking about forgiveness and everything and anything that bothered us about our situation. (beat) You know Jesse Clay didn't intend to kill your husband. Both of you need to resolve this so you don't stay stuck in your pain. You both have to let go of this awful thing in order to heal and be free of it all.

Michele: You had your sister to help you. George was all I had.

Kenny: Now is all we have. I know that everything that happened is back there somewhere in a dead past that can never be changed. I had to train my mind to live in the present and to be grateful for the things I have.

Michele: All I have is this business and I can't do it alone. My only employee quit and nobody wants to work for minimum wage.

Kenny looks at his wrist watch.

Kenny: I've got some time.

*****

216

SERIES OF SHOTS:

Later, in Michele's shop, Kenny, now wearing a smock, shampoos a dog on a back room table as Michele trims the nails of another dog as Don Williams sings "That's The Thing About Love" throughout this series of shots.

Later, Kenny blow dries another dog while brushing its coat as Michele is on the phone writing down an appointment time.

Later, Kenny shampoos another dog while Michele trims the nails of another dog.

Later, Kenny sweeps the back room floor as Michele gives another dog a haircut.

Later, Kenny takes a leash to the holding area and behind a dog cage he sees a massive muzzled Rottweiler. Kenny reads the name card on the front of cage: Felix, then warily opens the cage door, attaches the leash and struggles with getting Felix onto the shampoo table until Michele helps him.

Later, Kenny shampoos the muzzled Felix as Michele takes a payment from a customer at her front desk.

At closing time, exhausted Kenny refuses money Michele wants to pay him. Kenny exits her shop after he leaves his release form on her counter.

Haggard Kenny is walking to his Mustang when Michele exits her shop and hurries over to Kenny, handing him the signed release form. They smile at each other.

Next day, Kenny is in a men's clothing store looking at his reflection in a full-length mirror when trying on new clothes as Kansas smiles her approval.

That night, Gary, Kansas, and Kenny are seated at a cluttered table in Gary's front room of his cottage; they are going over Jesse Clay's file. Gary shows Kenny a pic of Tory Johns, Jesse Clay's ex-girlfriend, as Gary goes over the script he's written for Kenny.

A bit later, Kenny rehearses the script with Kansas and Gary in the cottage as the music fades out.

END SERIES OF SHOTS

*****

NEXT DAY

Kenny drives through a poor Wichita neighborhood and parks his car in front of a little run-down house. The front yard is skirted by a chain link fence. Kenny gets out of his Mustang wearing his new clothes, and upon reaching the front gate he sees a sign that reads: "NO TRESPASSING, BEWARE OF DOG". Kenny looks around the front yard from the sidewalk and doesn't see a dog. Before opening the front gate:

    Kenny: Anybody home?

Just then: Kenny sees a curtain move behind a front room window of this cracker box house. Kenny waits for someone to come outside. But then: the front door opens a bit and out comes a barking Rottweiler, the same dog Kenny recently groomed in Michele's shop.

    Kenny: Felix?

Felix recognizes Kenny and becomes friendly, wagging his tail and whining as Kenny reaches over the fence and pets the dog. Soon, TORY JOHNS, 30s, rough-living Caucasian, opens her door and can't believe her guard dog is friendly to this stranger. She calls out from her front door as Felix lick's Kenny's hand.

218

Tory (gruffly): What do you want?

Kenny: Are you Tory Johns?

Tory: Who wants to know?

Kenny: My name is Kenny Long! I work for G. K. Fleming, the independent writer/filmmaker!

Tory steps out of her house and approaches Kenny.

Tory: Did you give my dog something?

Kenny: No. Coincidentally, I gave Felix a bath yesterday at Michele's Pet Grooming shop.

Tory is caught off-guard.

*****

A bit later, Kenny sneaks a peek at Gary's checklist script on a 3x5 card while he's seated on a cluttered sofa in Tory's messy front room with Felix panting passively beside Kenny. Now Tory enters the front room from the kitchen and gives her guest a glass of water. Tory sits down on a chair, lights a cigarette and looks over Kenny's release form.

Tory: Let me get this straight. You want me to be in this documentary, and tell how I feel about Jesse Clay today?

Kenny: Right.

Tory: For what reason?

Kenny: Well, Jesse gets out of prison in about ten days and Mr. Fleming will interview you to get your take on his release and how you feel about Jesse today.

Tory: I sure as hell don't want to see Jesse Clay again. The guy's obviously a nut case. And that poor Mr. Townsend … and his wife.

Kenny: I'm curious. Does Michele know who you are when you bring Felix in to her shop? I mean, does she know you are Jesse's ex-girlfriend?

Tory: No. At least I don't think she does. (beat) You're probably wondering why I take my dog to her shop?

Kenny nods yes.

Tory: I feel sorry for her. I mean, I was the reason Jesse was there that day. So I take my dog there and give her a little business. I know it's not much, but I don't have much. And like I say, I feel sorry for her.

Kenny: Weren't you at Jesse's trial?

Tory: Yeah, but I was thirty pounds heavier and a bleached blonde. And I don't use my real name when I take Felix in to her shop. I pay cash.

Tory sees Kenny take a peek at his 3x5 card.

Kenny: Michele's going to be interviewed. I mean, the purpose of this documentary is to help resolve issues and healing if possible for Jesse and his victims.

Tory: I don't consider myself a victim … at least not like Michele was. (butts cigarette) Have you seen Jesse lately?

Kenny: Yeah. He's already been interviewed and Mr. Fleming will show you the interview before he interviews you … if you want.

Tory: So I can sign this and he comes here to interview me?

220

Kenny: Yeah, but you can have the interview anywhere.

Tory: Yeah, I don't want cameras in here.

Kenny: That's cool.

Tory looks at the release form and surprises Kenny by asking him for a pen. Kenny is relieved as she signs the release form; then he sneaks a look at his cheat card before saying:

Kenny: Put today's date next to your signature and your phone number with the best time to contact you to set up the interview.

After filling out the form, Kenny stands, gets the form from her and pets Felix goodbye.

Kenny (leaving): We'll be in touch soon. Have a good day.

Kenny exits the house feeling good about his meeting with Tory.

*****

A while later, just after Kenny returned home after getting Tory's release form signed, Kenny sits at the dining room table as Kansas serves him a sandwich she made him. Kansas sits down across from him. They are both excited.

Kansas: Talk about a chance to clear some karma. What are the odds you'd break the ice with Tory Johns because you shampooed her dog in Michele's shop? (amazed) Kenny, the universe is working through you, all because you were open and giving by helping Michele in her shop. Don't you see that?

Kenny (eating): Yeah. Like you always say: *There are no coincidences.* And that really hit me when I saw Felix in Tory's yard.

Kansas (animated): Don't you see what the universe is showing us? That we can do good work without a target. Tory has reached

221

out to Michele by taking Felix to her shop and we get a chance to help all of them manifest healing. This can only help Jesse when he gets out.

Kenny: I'm starting to believe in all your New Age talk.

Kansas smiles and looks at the two signed release forms she picks up from the table.

Kansas: I just got this incredible idea.

Kansas gets up from the table.

Kansas: I've got to set up the interview times with Michele and Tory. Good work, brother.

As Kansas walks away from the table:

Kenny (chewing): Thanks.

*****

In Bingham visiting area, tattooed ex-con JOHN BLACKBURN, 40, sits across the private glass viewing window waiting for inmate David Slovik, the same man denied parole at his recent hearing because of Joe Long's crew that interviewed Slovik's elderly victim, who pleaded on camera to parole board members not to release Slovik. Muscular Slovik is escorted to visiting area by an officer and sits across from his visitor, Blackburn. They talk discreetly.

Slovik: You'll see his kids visit him, coming and going with camera equipment. (leans closer to glass divider) I don't care how you do it ... take 'em both out.

Blackburn stands and leaves the visitor's area.

*****

Meanwhile, in the empty Bingham dining hall, Bob meets Joe for coffee alone at a table.

Bob: Okay, what's this good news?

Joe (proud father): He got 'em.

Bob: Who got what?

Joe: Kenny. He got both release forms signed.

Bob is impressed and admits:

Bob: I didn't think he'd get one.

Joe: Gary wrote down a checklist script for him to follow … and he closed both of them on the first visit.

Bob: Well I'll be damned. (beat) When are the interviews?

Joe: Kansas set 'em both for tomorrow.

Bob shakes his head back and forth, amazed at the crew's speed and efficiency.

Bob: You figure out that surprise ending for Jesse Clay yet?

Joe: Yeah. But if I tell you … it won't be a surprise, will it?

*****

SERIES OF SHOTS:

Next morning, Kansas's Jeep is parked outside Michele's Pet Grooming shop. Kansas video tapes Gary's interview with Michele Townsend in Michele's little office in the back room as Kenny shampoos a dog.

Later, outside Michele's shop, Gary and Kansas carry equipment to the Jeep as Michele hugs Kenny goodbye.

223

Later, the crew has lunch in a café; they're talking about the upcoming interview with Tory Johns, Clay's ex-girlfriend.

Later that day, in a small city park, Kenny takes muzzled and leashed Felix for a walk as Kansas tapes the Tory Johns interview with Gary at a picnic tabled shelter area.

Later, as Kansas and Gary load the Jeep with equipment after the interview, Kenny waves goodbye to Tory and Felix. When Kenny goes over to the Jeep, the crew has a group hug to celebrate a successful day.

Later that evening at home, Kansas edits today's interviews at the dining room table as:

Gary writes in his recliner in the cottage front room.

Next morning, Kenny waits in his parked car in the hospital parking lot as:

Gary finishes his visit with recovering Melissa in a hospital psyche ward. Melissa hugs Gary goodbye as:

Joe watches with keen interest the edited interviews with Michele and Tory at his desk in his private cell.

Later, Kenny drops off Gary at the cottage and drives off. Gary unlocks Traveller's back door; he goes into the bathroom, finds his pot stash and dumps it into his toilet.

*****

Next morning, at Joe's private table on the Bingham prison grounds, Bob and Joe stand nearby while Jesse Clay watches the interviews with Michele and Tory on Joe's laptop. Gary sits across from Jesse at Joe's table waiting to interview Jesse as Kansas and Kenny videotape Jesse watching the end of Tory's interview. It's obvious that Jesse is touched by the interviews as he drops his head and cries into his hands. Gary patiently waits as Jesse wipes his eyes with his sleeves and composes himself. The cameras are on.

Jesse Clay: Sorry.

Gary: Don't apologize ... we all need a good cry now and then. (beat) What was it that got to you in Michele's interview?

Jesse Clay: I guess I didn't expect Michele to forgive me. (beat) I never cried for her loss until now. (beat) In here ... you can get lost in your anger and resentment. But that stuff is denial, a smokescreen where your mind tries to tell you that you can pay your debt with time. That's another lie: that time heals all wounds. I don't want to leave here with a chip on my shoulder like a lot of guys in here. Forgiveness, that's something I couldn't get for myself until Michele ...

More tears for Jesse.

Gary: How do you feel about your ex-girlfriend, Tory, after watching her interview?

Jesse Clay: I get it how abusive I was with my anger. I mean, she got that Rottweiler for protection from me when I get out. And I don't blame her. In here, if you really want to change you have to learn that fear and anger are related ... and there's too much of that in here and out there. No sir ... time alone doesn't help.

Jesse hangs his head again and sobs into his hands. Joe sees that his crew is touched by Jesse's emotional candor.

Joe (off screen to crew): Good!

Joe and his crew go over to Jesse and console him with a group hug. Then Bob escorts Jesse back to his cell as the crew gathers around Joe's table.

Joe: Kansas, after you edit this and put it all together, Kenny, I want you to personally deliver disc copies to Michele and Tory. I want a copy to give Warden Ted, who will present it to The Board. Of course keep a master copy.

Kansas gives a positive nod.

Joe (to Kansas): I want two more copies. One for Jesse and one express mailed to this address.

Joe hands Kansas a piece of paper.

Joe: Okay, this is the close. We're not finished until the DVD is in the hands of all concerned. Any questions?

Gary: Can I have a copy?

Joe: Sure.

Gary helps Kenny and Kansas pack up their equipment.

*****

SERIES OF SHOTS:

A bit later, someone uses binoculars to watch the crew load their equipment into the Jeep on Bingham parking lot. As Jeep exits Bingham grounds, John Blackburn, the same ex-con that Slovik ordered to "*take 'em out,*" follows the Jeep in his black Nissan with tinted windows all around.

Looking through binoculars in his parked Nissan, Blackburn watches the crew enter Gary's cottage. Blackburn sees the Mustang, Jeep, and Traveller parked outside the cottage.

Later that night, inside the cottage's cozy front room, Gary watches Kansas edit Jesse's documentary as Kenny watches a movie from Gary's recliner.

226

Later the same night, Kenny has fallen asleep in Gary's recliner watching TV as Kansas finishes putting Jesse's documentary into DVD cases and Gary covers Kenny with a blanket. Kansas stands, yawns and stretches before going into Gary's bedroom to sleep as Gary goes outside the cottage, unlocks Traveller's back door upon deciding to sleep in his RV tonight. The sound of Traveller's back door closing shut wakes Blackburn, who was asleep while sitting behind the wheel of his Nissan with his window rolled down. Blackburn didn't see Gary enter Traveller; he sees the Jeep and Mustang still parked where they were and the lights are all out in the cottage. Blackburn lights a cigarette and drives away.

The next day, Joe watches Jesse's documentary with Warden Ted in the warden's office as:

Kenny delivers a DVD to Michele at her shop.

Later that day, Kenny pets Felix goodbye and Tory waves goodbye to Kenny from her front door after Kenny has delivered the DVD to her.

Later, we see split-screen shots of Michele and Tory watching the DVD with keen interest at home.

END SERIES OF SHOTS

*****

A week later, it's Jesse Clay's release day. In Bingham's inmate processing station, Bob gives Jesse Clay, dressed in civilian clothes, a paper bag that holds his scanty valuables and escorts Jesse outside the prison walls of Bingham.

Outside Bingham, Bob walks with Jesse to Bob's nearby parked truck. Jesse gets into Bob's truck and Bob drives them off the prison grounds. Inside Bob's moving truck:

Jesse Clay (elated): What service. I never expected to get a ride out of here to the bus station.

While leaving the Bingham grounds, Bob hands Jesse a DVD copy of his documentary.

Bob: Joe wanted you to have a copy.

Jesse Clay: Thanks. Jesse puts his DVD into his bag; then Jesse is confused when Bob pulls over his truck and parks behind an idling produce truck marked: "Grand Junction Produce Co."

Bob: That's your new employer.

Jesse is confused.

Bob: Joe sent your DVD to Ron Burns; he owns Grand Junction Produce. He needs a driver and wants you to start out in the warehouse until you get licensed and you can drive for him. This is your ride to Grand Junction.

Jesse Clay (stunned): I don't know what to say.

Bob (kidding on the level): Don't say anything. And don't come back.

As the truck driver gets out of his cab and walks toward Bob's truck.

Jesse Clay: Tell Joe thanks for everything.

Bob: I will. You take care.

They shake hands and Jesse gets out of the truck with his bag. Bob watches the friendly truck driver and Jesse shake hands before Jesse hustles to the cab of the truck and climbs up and onto the front passenger seat. Bob smiles as the truck drives away, then Bob speed dials "Gary" on his cell phone and Gary's voice mail comes on:

228

Gary (voice mail recording): *Leave a message.*

After the beep:

   Bob (on cell phone): Fishing party at Gary's tonight! I'll bring the beer and pizza, and you bring the bait. Call me.

Bob closes his phone and drives back toward Bingham.

End of Episode 5